GW00656594

The Lore of Flowers

The Lore of Flowers

NEIL EWART

Illustrated by
Nina O'Connell

BLANDFORD PRESS
Poole   Dorset

First published in the U.K. 1982 by Blandford Press,
Link House, West Street, Poole, Dorset, BH15 1LL.

Copyright © 1982 Neil Ewart

Distributed in the United States by
Sterling Publishing Co., Inc.,
2 Park Avenue, New York, N.Y. 10016.

British Library Cataloguing in Publication Data

Ewart, Neil
 The lore of flowers.
 1. Flowers
 I. Title
 582.13   QK85.5

ISBN 0 7137 1176 0

All rights reserved. No part of this book may
be reproduced or transmitted in any form or by
any means, electronic or mechanical, including
photocopying, recording or any information storage
and retrieval system, without permission in
writing from the Publisher.

Typeset by Keyspools Ltd, Golborne, Lancs.

Printed by Toppan Printing Co. (S) Pte Ltd. Singapore

Contents

If a man could pass through Paradise in a dream
and have a flower presented to him as a pledge
that his soul had really been there, and if he
found that flower in his hand when he awoke —
                                    Aye, and what then?

                    Coleridge

Wallflowers

Said Time, 'I cannot bear the flowers,
    They spoil the look of old decay;
They cover all my ruined towers,
    My fallen shrines, and abbeys grey:
I'll cut them down—why should they grow?
    I marvel Death upon his graves
Allows so many buds to blow!
    O'er all my works the Wallflower waves!'—
His scythe he sharpened as he spoke,
And deeper frowned at every stroke.

'Old man,' said Love, 'the flowers are mine;
    Leave them alone and go thy way—
Destruction is the work of thine,
    'Tis mine to beautify decay.
Is't not enough that thou hast power
    To lay both youth and beauty low,
But thou must envy the poor flower
    Which scarce a day sees in full blow?
I've seen thee smile on them for hours!'—
''Tis true,' said Time, and spared the flowers.

Thomas Miller

ALTHOUGH TIME has been given power over the works of man, over those of nature he holds no sway. For from the very flowers that perish others spring up, such as wallflowers, which refuse to lie dormant and bring life back to ancient stone ruins of castle, turret, arch and wall.

Wallflowers belong to the cheerful family of 'old-fashioned' flowers, obviously taking their name from the fact that they thrive on walls which they adorn in a most extravagant and delightful manner, making them mountains of perfume, and beacons of fire. More than this, when all beside them have perished and decayed, when the carved and vaulted roof has mouldered away, when the tall turret has fallen, stone by stone, and crumbled into dust, wallflowers will still wave above the buried ruins— bending over, contemplating desolation through long centuries.

Whether the wallflower is a true native of Britain or was introduced during the Roman invasion, or later during the Norman Conquest, remains uncertain. We do know, however, that the wallflower, or *Cheiranthus cheiri*

Wallflowers

(to use its Latin name, meaning hand-flower) was carried as a nosegay at festivals in the Middle Ages because of its sweet scent.

We also know that wallflowers were planted on castle walls near windows so the aroma could seep through the open slits to bring pleasant fragrance to the rooms. In this, on one occasion, according to legend, lay a tragic story. Elizabeth, daughter of the Earl of March, betrothed to the heir of Robert III of Scotland, fell in love with the son of a border chieftan. One day, disguised as a wandering minstrel he sang to her beneath her room in the castle of Neidpath, on the banks of the Tweed, near Peebles, in which she was imprisoned. In his song he told her to reach for a wallflower growing near the window and drop it at his feet if she wished to elope with him. As she did so, she lost her balance in her excitement, and fell to the ground and was killed. Overcome with grief from such sudden loss, her lover left the country to travel as a minstrel all over Europe, wearing a wallflower in memory of her whenever they were in bloom. The idea was copied by other minstrels and, thus, the flower became the symbol of faithfulness in adversity.

The Large Gardens and Estates

POETS HAVE ALWAYS likened gardens to paradise and done so, through the ages, not only to conjure up heavenly visions and a state of supreme bliss but appropriately, for paradise is an ancient Persian word—still to be found in our dictionaries—meaning garden or park.

The most famous gardens of all, and among the Seven Wonders of the ancient world, were the Hanging Gardens of Babylon. They were built by King Nebuchadnezzar, around 660 B.C., to please his wife who had come from a hilly land and wearied of the flat plains of Babylon. They consisted of vast stone terraces constructed, one on top of the other, some rising to 300 ft, on which were planted gardens of beautiful tropical flowers, exotic blooms, groves and avenues of palm trees; water was pumped from the river Euphrates to irrigate them.

Long before then, Tiglath-Pileser, one of the greatest Assyrian kings who lived about 1100 B.C., was bringing trees from foreign lands, from the forty-two countries he claimed to have conquered, to decorate his parks and gardens.

The ancient Greek and Romans cultivated decorative and useful plants being the first to grow them in pots, and introduced statues and fountains into their gardens. The ancient civilizations of China and Japan took the development of their gardens to the heights of art and tranquility with their exotic blooms, quiet pools and streams, bridges, rockeries and pagodas— perfect settings where inspiration and refreshment for both mind and body could be found.

England had walled gardens during medieval times but, apart from trees and hedges, these contained herbs mostly used for their healing properties and for culinary purposes. Developments during the Tudor period took giant strides with flowers planted among the grass and in neat flower-beds, with clipped hedges, straight paths and arbours. The great gardens of the Italian Renaissance, which had become established nearer home in France, were beginning to have influence and be copied on the larger English estates—flower-beds being shaped in precise geometrical shapes and patterns, surrounded by mown grass and coloured gravels. Statues, pools and fountains provided additional features of interest. With such formality there would seem little place for 'horse-play', but the people of those times enjoyed a joke and frequently placed fountains in out of the way places where visitors could be sprayed unexpectedly with water as they passed by.

Mazes, in which guests could lose their way for hours in the complex network of paths between a mass of tall trim hedges, were also popular. In ecclesiastical circles the significance of the maze has been interpreted as our journey through life. The distance travelled along the paths of the maze represent the months and years of our time. The junctions are the decisions we have to face, with the wrong turnings standing for the mistakes we make, and the centre symbolizing heaven.

During Elizabethan times knott gardens came into fashion. These were rather like miniature mazes with fancy-shaped flower borders separated by tiny hedges of clipped box only a few inches tall. A replica of one of the designs of those days can be seen at 'New Place' gardens, Stratford-upon-Avon, where the foundations of the house which Shakespeare bought, and to which he subsequently retired in 1610, are preserved. It was also the house where he died in 1616. Although no part of the house remains, the knott garden in this delightful setting provides a fine example of the intricate pattern of flowers, sweet-smelling herbs, and dwarf hedges. Many modern gardeners have constructed knott gardens—but it is something that has to be planned and done carefully as the tiny hedges must be continuous, with no loose ends.

Flower gardens, up until Stuart times, continued to consist of formal geometrical designs, mainly of rectangles, crescent-shapes and squares divided by wide paths, and walks with the grand vista capable of being seen and enjoyed when viewed from the mansion. Lawns were known as 'sporting garden plots', because they were places where the ladies and gentlemen might 'disport themselves' when the weather was fine.

Indoor gardening had begun and become well established when greenhouses were introduced in the reign of William and Mary at the end of the 17th century. Although described at the time 'as a very curious contrivance to raise and preserve tender plants', they soon transformed the gardening scene, as successful attempts were made to propagate exciting new species of flora from the East and the Americas. The Romans were the first to make use of hot air flues in specially constructed 'warm houses' before introducing tubes for hot-water pipe heating in order to procure blooms out of season. The early greenhouses in England were known as 'stove-houses' and the real development of green- or glasshouses as we know them today had to wait until the 18th century when designs were improved largely by the botanical gardeners, and the more wealthy landowners who brought finance and refinements to create more modern hot-water systems.

The father of landscape gardening was William Kent, an 18th-century architect, who conceived designs for both mansions and the countryside around them, not as single entities, but as a whole, one being complementary to the other. A contemporary, and one time partner of Kent, was 'Capability' Brown—the most famous English landscape gardener of all. His real name was Lancelot, but he became known as 'Capability' because he never failed to talk about the capabilities of the grounds he was asked to landscape—his skilful and imaginative eye could always see 'great capabilities for improvement'. Today, with fully developed trees, mature landscapes, and all the aids of modern machinery to mow finely the vast acreage of lawns, and to pump the water more purposefully from fountains, we are the fortunate inheritors who can now see these fine gardens at their best and in the way they were intended.

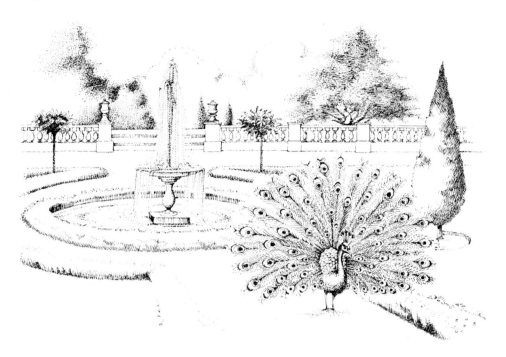

Among the many gardens designed by Capability Brown there are those at Kew, near London, Blenheim Palace in Oxfordshire, the birthplace of Sir Winston Churchill; and the lovely 'Backs', or gardens of the colleges by the river at Cambridge. These are fine memorials to a man, later appointed Royal Gardener, who managed to create natural effects by artificial means and yet retain harmony with nature.

The herbaceous border was an English idea which came into being during Victorian times—the wealth of the gentry was measured by the number of plants in their garden beds, which ranged from 10,000 to 50,000 or more. Apart from this vulgar form of ostentation, there was a great demand for flowers, particularly scented ones, to decorate the spacious halls, dining-

Estate garden in the style. landscaped by Capability Brown.

rooms and ballrooms, as well as for ladies' personal adornment and gentlemen's buttonholes. There was also a great upsurge in indoor gardening, with the inevitable boom in conservatories and winter gardens.

Many fruits continued to be grown, as they were in Tudor times, and most of the larger houses had vines. England excelled in producing finer grapes for the table than any other country ever since artificial heat was applied. The vinery of the Duke of Portland, at Welbeck in Nottinghamshire, produced a bunch of Syrian grapes weighing over 19 lbs. and was sent by the duke as a present to the Marquis of Rockingham at Wentworth House. Four labourers carried it on a staff, by turns, over the distance of 20 miles. The red Hamburg vine at Hampton Court was famous for years and had been known to produce 2,200 bunches weighing an average of one pound each. Vines attain a great age and as a vineyard one hundred years old was reckoned to be young, the Victorians inherited many mature vines.

The ancient Greeks honoured Dionysus—the god of the vineyard, of trees and fruitfulness. The Romans knew the god of wine as Bacchus, who travelled from country to country teaching men to cultivate the grape and to make wine. In Rome the Bacchanalia, or festival of Bacchus, was celebrated every third year until 186 B.C. Since then man has perfected ways of making wine from all manner of fruits, vegetables and flowers, both cultivated and wild.

Few sights are more inspiring than Wisteria in full flower and, like the vine, the plant has a long life. Many of the blooms which can be seen today climbing on buildings and growing in the gardens of the older estates belong to wisterias planted a century or more ago.

The 'Crown Imperial', which is a member of the great family of lilies and one of the oldest known cultivated plants, was thought much of by the grand old gardeners of Elizabethan and Stuart times. According to legend it was the only flower, amongst many others growing in the Garden of Gethsemane, which failed to bow its head as Christ passed by. Since when it has hung its head in shame with tears in its eyes. The tears which can be seen to this day at the base of each bell refuse to fall from the drooping flowers even when shaken, or swaying in the wind. The tears are, in fact, nectar.

'Crown Imperial' has been dedicated to St Edward the martyr and king who ruled for three years from A.D. 975. Until he was murdered at his step-mother's behest—he was stabbed by a servant at Corfe Castle in Dorset—in order to bring her son Ethelred the Unready to the throne. The plant flowers in the spring and blooms on or around 18 March—St Edward's day.

Neither the Rhododendron nor the Azalea, which is akin to it, seen growing in parks and gardens as well as in the wild, are native to Britain. They came mainly from China, Japan, Turkey, Europe and North America. The rhododendron was introduced about the middle of the 17th century and many of the choicest varieties were obtained by crossing the ordinary purple-flowered rhododendron with the more brilliant Himalayan and American kinds. The 'Coast Rhododendron' is the state Flower of Washington, while the azalea is the national flower of Belgium.

Gladioli can be found everywhere which isn't surprising because it is the world's second most popular cut flower (the rose is number one). Gladius means sword—descriptive of the shape of the leaves.

Another popular flower, which adds grace and beauty to any garden, is the Lupin—which was cultivated in European and English gardens, after being introduced from North America, almost 350 years ago. One perennial form growing on the Pacific Coast continues to live for up to ten years.

Some species still grow wild in Britain, but the biggest step forward in Lupin cultivation came with the introduction of the Russell lupins—perfected by George Russell, a modest English countryman and jobbing gardener. The art of horticulture knows no barrier of age, it seems, for he did not start hybridising and selecting until he was 60 years old, and continued for 20 years before being satisfied. The result was worth waiting for because it brought a wonderful range of colours with the finest flowers.

Lupin seeds have been used as food by man as well as for cattle since ancient times. But according to Virgil (70–19 B.C.), the great Roman poet, unless the seeds are boiled in several waters they are so bitter that the face of anyone eating them becomes painfully contorted, with tears streaming from their eyes. A writer of 150 years or so ago said lupin seeds were so poisonous that they had been known to kill a hippopotamus.

The use of plants for medicinal purposes stretches back thousands of years and amongst them there were always those that were harmful, poisonous, and which could even kill. Finding out which were beneficial and which were not has taken its toll, but it is surprising how much knowledge was discovered and recorded about the healing properties of plants as far back as 4,000 years ago. By the first century A.D. tremendous advances had been made when Dioscorides, the Greek naturalist and physician, wrote *De Materia Medica* identifying over 600 plants and their properties and uses, which remained the most authoritative text on pharmacology for sixteen centuries.

Although a lot of sense, and nonsense, has been written about plants there is no doubt that their healing properties, and use as flavourings for food, continued to remain uppermost in the minds of gardeners throughout the

Azaleas and rhododendrons.

ages. In the present century plants are still saving lives, prolonging them, and enabling people to lead active lives who, without them, would long since have departed.

Few gardens are without herbs these days, whether a large area is devoted to them or just a small pot or two. Besides any healing powers they may have and their use as an ingredient in good cookery, they are a joy to look at besides providing many other advantages. Once Woodruff is picked and dried, for instance, it gives off a delightful smell of new-mown hay and honey. During the 15th century garlands of woodruff were hung in churches, and also in linen cupboards where they were said to keep moths away. In Georgian times, when the gentry opened their pocket-watches they were able to enjoy the fragrance from woodruff leaves placed within the cases.

Southernwood, with its French name of *garde-robe* (wardrobe), was also used for keeping moths away from clothes, besides being a popular herb in nosegays because of its stimulating aroma. Angelica, which was very popular in English gardens 400 years ago, had many uses, including one recommendation in which the seeds should be burnt in a 'fire-pan' in order to impart a refreshing scent throughout the home.

Sage is used mostly today in stuffings, but in the more romantic days of the language of flowers it represented esteem. So called, no doubt, because the sages and philosophers of old were held in high esteem for their gravity and wisdom. It was believed to bring long life to anyone who made frequent use of it. Fennel also conveyed longevity, and was used by competitors in the Greek Olympics to increase their strength. The builders of the Pyramids ate a clove of Garlic each day, for the same reason.

Tansy, which has been grown for hundreds of years, is still a popular plant in herb gardens. One of its most curious uses in olden times was as an insect repellant, in which it was rubbed on joints of meat to keep the flies away. Tansy puddings, cakes and omlettes were relished in days gone past but fell out of fashion a century ago. Although the plant derives its name from the Greek word for immortality, it contains poisons. It is fairly common in the wild throughout Britain and grows in abundance in Hampshire, in the south of England, where it is gathered for destruction each year before it can harm the free-roaming New Forest ponies. It is still cultivated in many gardens, though, if only for the attractive ornamental value of its golden-yellow flower-heads.

Daffodils

I wandered lonely as a cloud
That floats on high o'er vales and hills,
When all at once I saw a crowd,
A host, of golden daffodils;
Beside the lake, beneath the trees,
Fluttering and dancing in the breeze.

William Wordsworth

THE COMMON DAFFODIL which heralds the arrival of spring is a species of the narcissus—beloved by the ancients and poets. Whether it is one of Britain's true native plants or was introduced by the Romans, few seem certain.

'Affodyl' and 'daffadowndyllyes' were some of the early English names. In Elizabethan times the wild daffodil grew so prolifically in the fields near London that the market women of Cheapside used large circular baskets on their heads to carry them into the city to sell each day for a few pennies a bunch—town dwellers today still buy the small wild variety of daffodil.

It was not until the beginning of this century that the Welsh adopted the daffodil as their national flower. Originally, the modest leek was worn as the badge of honour on 1 March—the day of their patron saint, St David. During the Welsh wars a party of Welshmen wanted a mark of distinction. As they passed through a field of leeks, they seized the plants and stuck them in their caps, and under this signal they were victorious. The daffodil was officially adopted as their national flower at the investitute of Edward, Prince of Wales, in 1911, because the leek was considered vulgar by some. The leek, however, is still worn as the official insignia on the uniforms of the Welsh Guards on St David's Day.

Just over a century ago, 150 varieties of daffodil were offered in a nurseryman's catalogue at prices ranging from five shillings to a penny per bulb. Today, more than 10,000 cultivated varieties of daffodil, jonquil and narcissus are grown and treasured as garden flowers.

Greek myths tell of the beautiful youth, Narcissus, who, because he had spurned the love of Echo, was condemned by Aphrodite to lose his heart to his own image reflected in a clear pool. Fascinated, he gazed day and night at the beautiful apparition becoming weaker and weaker from lack of food, until he pined away and died. The gods in compassion then changed him into the lovely flower that grows near quiet pools.

Daffodils, narcissi and white jonquil.

The Appeal of Bells

THE SHAPES AND PATTERNS of flowers arouse a sense of wonder and awe as we study them more closely; few are more interesting, or inspirational, than those resembling the shape of bells.

One of the best known and most loved is the Canterbury Bell, so named because it not only grew plentifully in olden times in that part of Kent, but also because it resembled the smaller bells which Chaucer's pilgrims used for decorating the harnesses of their horses.

The Campanula family of bell-shaped flowers contains some 300 species but, apart from the Canterbury Bell and the Harebell, bell-shapes—with or without their hammers—are to be found outside this vast family: in the Bluebell, Columbine, Convolvulus, some of the Ericas, Fuchsia, and the Martagon Lily (before opening); and with hammers after opening, in the Gentian, the Snake's Head Fritillary, the White Fritillary, and the Anemone (blanda)—before fully open. These are but a few from a seemingly endless list.

The bell-shapes and different colours and patterns are not just ornamental, but functional, helping the plants to survive by attracting bees and moths,

and certain insects, while repelling others. The bell-shape of the blossoms, when drooped during rain, serves to protect the pollen.

The old-fashioned flower, the Canterbury Bell—so long a favourite of cottage gardens—is still popular today with many good strains and varieties and a wide range of colours available from blue to pure white, including pink, rose and mauve.

Spring Flowers

Along the blushing borders bright with dew,
And in yon mingled wilderness of flowers,
Fair-handed Spring unbosoms every grace:
Throws out the snow-drop and the crocus first;
The daisy, primrose, violet darkly blue,
And polyanthus of unnumbered dyes;
The yellow wall-flower, stained with iron brown,
And lavish stock that scents the garden round:
From the soft wing of vernal breezes shed,
Anemonies; ariculas, enriched
With shining meal o'er all their velvet leaves;
And full ranunculas, of glowing red.
Then comes the tulip-race, where Beauty plays
Her idle freaks: from family diffused
To family, as flies the feather-dust,
The varied colours run; and while they break
On the charmed eye, the exulting florist marks,
With secret pride, the wonders of his hand.
No gradual bloom is wanting; from the bud,
First-born of Spring, to Summer's musky tribes:
Nor hyacinths, deep-purpled; nor jonquils,
Of potent fragrance; nor narcissus fair,
As o'er the fabled fountain hanging still;
Nor broad carnations, nor gay-spotted pinks;
Nor, showered from every bush, the damask-rose:
Infinite numbers, delicacies, smells,
With hues on hues expression cannot paint,
The breath of Nature, and her endless bloom.

James Thomson

Primulas.

Primulas

THE POET Thomson's 'polyanthus of unnumbered dyes', which have been growing in gardens since the 17th century, is a British creation which came into being as a result of a cross between the primrose and the cowslip. The scientific name *Primula* comes from *primus*, meaning first, which refers to the early flowering time.

The original colours were purple or brown but as their popularity grew, and an exciting range of other colours were introduced by the plant breeders, the interest spread to working men who were willing to pay £1 a plant—as much as, and in some cases more than, they earned in a week.

Another primula, the Auricula, was also cultivated enthusiastically by workers in northern England who formed societies and held exhibitions. This was a native of Switzerland and the Alps and after spreading through Europe it is believed to have been introduced into Britain by the Huguenot refugees and afterwards cultivated intensively by the British weavers and miners in those areas of Cheshire and Lancashire where the Huguenots had originally settled. Prices of plants were mostly about £1, but some owned by the well-to-do were valued as highly as £20. The auricula's popularity continued to spread through the land and the National Auricula Society was eventually founded in 1872.

A medicine made from the roots is reputed to have been used by mountaineers in the Alps to ward off attacks of vertigo. Although primulas grow at sea level, many from the Himalayas and Far East have no fear of heights themselves and thrive at altitudes of 17,000 feet.

The Cowslip (which is mentioned in the chapter on hedgerows) besides being praised by the poets for its beauty and fragrance, was also acclaimed by the early herbalists as having the ability to pass on these qualities to humans. Culpeper, the 17th-century herbalist and doctor, who believed that there was a plant to cure everything, wrote: '... and our city dames know well enough the ointment or distilled water of it adds to beauty, or at least restores it when it is lost'.

Culpeper, though sincere, tended to be over enthusiastic about the power of plants. However, ladies for whom they did not work could always console themselves by using the cowslip to make one of the most subtle and pleasing of all country wines.

Snowdrops and Crocuses

FEW FLOWERS can be more welcome than Snowdrops and Crocuses which arrive as harbingers to tell us that winter is awakening from its long sleep.

First to arrive, as the emblem of hope, the snowdrop gives us encouragement after the dark, cold months. The early spring crocuses appear shortly afterwards, as symbols of youthfulness, with the reassurance of fresh life and the promise of better things to come.

According to legend the snowdrop became the symbol of hope when Adam and Eve were expelled from the Garden of Eden. With their progress slowed in the heavy snow, a forlorn and exhausted Eve had neither the strength nor will to go further, believing that every day in future would be the same . . . with never-ending winters. At the depth of her despair, an angel appeared who transformed some of the falling snow-flakes into the flowers of the snowdrop and gave proof that winters do have their end and give way to spring.

Another story about this emblem of hope takes us back to the Civil Wars. Wealthy estates were being confiscated daily by Cromwell, and the heir of many a noble line slept his long sleep upon the battlefield. Amongst them was the last of the Nevilles, who had died at the battle of Marston Moor.

When his siter, Ellen Neville, walked away from the ancient manor house, resigned for ever to handing over the home of her ancestors to a complete stranger, by command of the stern Protector, Oliver Cromwell, it was still early spring. As she gave a last farewell glance back through the massive iron gates of the gardens and park, her maid picked up a snowdrop which her mistress had dropped and said, 'Take heart; this flower is the emblem of Hope, and something tells me that you will yet live to see happier days.'

The young General Marchmont took possession of the splendid old mansion as a gift from those who then ruled the nation, and a reward for his unimpeached valour. He had been offered several of the Royalist's confiscated estates before, but refused them when he learnt that the rightful heirs were still alive, although in exile.

Marchmont could not be induced to take possession of the Neville house until the most solemn assurance had been given that not one of the family was then left alive. He did not know that such a person as Ellen Neville existed, for she had been educated in a remote part of the country and only returned to dwell there shortly before her brother's death.

Ellen Neville was too well versed in the changes those stormy times produced to be at all astonished at what had happened. She knew that she had suffered as others had done who had fallen from their high estate and, although a staunch Royalist, she had heard much in praise of the young general. With such knowledge, she soon became reconciled to her lot. By the time another spring had become summer, she had so overcome her old scruples that with the encouragement of her maid she ventured out now and then to walk in the park and gardens that recalled so many happy memories of her childhood. The gardens were still a picture, carefully tended by a young man who had belonged to the regiment which the General commanded and who would never allow the maid to depart, when in attendance on her young mistress, without persuading her to accept a splendid bouquet.

On one of those days, when her maid was gossiping with the young gardener, the Lady Ellen wandered alone down one of the long avenues to the old summerhouse. As she sat, musing on the happy hours she had spent there with her mother, she was startled by the appearance of a tall, handsome-looking gentleman who approached without observing her — so deeply was he absorbed in the book in his hand. It wasn't until she arose from her seat and her heavy silk dress rustled that he became aware of her. But once observed, he became mute and motionless in an instant, for there before him was someone like the lady in the enchanted chair he was then reading about in the *Mask of Comus*, given to him by no less a person than the great poet, John Milton, himself.

As she apologised for the intrusion, he was at first embarrassed, then at great pains to assure her that her presence was a pleasure, and would be so at all times and all seasons, whenever she chose to wander through the ancient gardens whose beauty, he regretted, was so seldom visited by anyone, save himself.

Many a happy hour did they spend together afterwards, seated side by side in the old summerhouse, as he read beautiful passages from the *Mask of Comus*. When he wasn't quoting, but gliding in conversation with ease from one subject to another, he still remained in complete ignorance of her rank and station, except that her whole family, with the exception of herself, had perished during the wars. As any further mention of the subject seemed to cause her pain, the young general ceased to question further.

With the approach of winter, the affairs of the nation called General Marchmont up to London to meet the assembled Parliament. With her uppermost in his thoughts, he wrote to her frequently. With the arrival of early spring, when he was released from his duties, he hastened back to the ancient manor house.

The Lady Ellen was walking in the alleys of the garden when he alighted from his horse to pay his respects to her before he entered the hall. As he took her hand, he thought that she had never before appeared so beautiful. Then noticing the few pale snowdrops which she held between the fingers in her other hand he said, with a smile, 'You are, like myself, well versed in the meanings which the old poets have attributed to the flowers. Within your fingers you will know that you hold the emblem of Hope. Give me one blossom that I, too, may hope . . .' He confessed his love, and was accepted. It came about on the same sunny morning that they were married they saw her faithful maid led to the altar by the honest gardener.

When crocuses arrive in their full splendour they seem to suprise the honey bees no less than ourselves; the noise the bees make as they brush up the pollen is like that of a gang of prospectors rendered half delirious by the discovery of a gold mine. And, indeed, it is a gold mine to them — or more precisely a bread mine, for the pollen becomes 'bee-bread' when in the hive.

The pollen is first used by the worker bees to produce a special food from the glands in their head to feed the young larvae. The pollen is later mixed with honey to provide 'bee-bread' upon which the larvae are able to feed themselves up to the point when they will emerge as perfect bees to join the general congregation.

Bee-keepers, they say, cannot have too many crocuses because, at the time

Snowdrops and crocuses.

they flower, the bees are more or less distressed and cannot travel far. It is of great help to them to find refreshment near home, and thus be enabled without risk to 'improve the shining hour'.

Some people manage to have crocuses which flower in almost every month of the year, but those who don't at least get a double helping of pleasure from this flower with the arrival of the Autumn Crocus.

According to Holinshed (whose *Chronicles of England, Scotland, and Ireland* were much used by Shakespeare and the Elizabethan dramatists as a historical source book for their plays), a certain young gentleman named *Krokos*, the Latin word for saffron, went 'to plaie at coits in the field with Mercurie, and being heedlesse of himselfe, Mercurie's coit mischanced to hit him on the head . . .' The 'coit' killed Krokos, and a saffron-bearing flower sprang from the ground where he had bled; the flower was named after Krokos to commemorate him. And that is the way the crocus got its name.

That piece of information, in itself, makes it all the harder to understand why the Saffron Crocus (variety of Autumn Crocus) should have been chosen as a symbol of mirth. But one of its effects, when taken as a herbal remedy in olden times, was that it provoked laughter and great merriment.

Saffron used to be a much prized commodity for use in drugs, as dyes for women's hair, and for colouring cloth. Henry VIII, however, passed a law prohibiting its use in the dyeing of linen sheets for the reason that coloured sheets tended to be washed less frequently. The king was a tyrant even in taste—making arbitrary laws to regulate the dress of his subjects. Cloth of gold was reserved for dukes and marquises; if of purple this was exclusively for the royal family. While silks and velvets were only to be worn by commoners of distinction, embroidery was forbidden to all beneath an earl.

The saffron grown in England, considered the best in the world, was established in abundance at Saffron Walden, Essex. Amongst its many uses, saffron was also greatly favoured for the colouring and flavouring of food. Every morning, as soon as the flower had opened in the sun, the orange coloured stigma, or centre part, was gathered. The upper part of the stigma was picked out, dried in a kiln, and made into cakes, and the rest of the flower was thrown away.

THE SNOWDROP

As Hope, with bowed head, silent stood,
    And on her golden anchor leant,
Watching below the angry flood,
    While Winter, 'mid the dreariment
Half-buried in the drifted snow,

Lay sleeping on the frozen ground,
Not heeding how the wind did blow,
    Bitter and bleak on all around:
She gazed on Spring, who at her feet
Was looking on the snow and sleet.

Spring sighed, and through the driving gale
    Her warm breath caught the falling snow,
And from the flakes a flower as pale
    Did into spotless whiteness blow;
Hope smiling saw the blossom fall,
    And watched its root strike in the earth—
'I will that flower the Snowdrop call,'
    Said Hope, 'In memory of its birth:
And through all ages it shall be
In reverence held, for love of me.'

'And ever from my hidden bowers,'
    Said Spring, 'it first of all shall go,
And be the herald of the flowers,
    To warn away the sheeted snow:
Its mission done, then by thy side
    All summer long it shall remain.
While other flowers I scatter wide,
    O'er every hill, and wood, and plain,
This shall return, and ever be
A sweet companion, Hope, for thee.'

Hope stooped and kissed her sister Spring,
    And said, 'For hours, when thou art gone,
I'm left alone without a thing
    That I can fix my heart upon;
'Twill cheer me many a lonely hour,
    And in the future I shall see
Those who would sink raised by that flower—
    They'll look on it, then think of thee:
And many a sadful heart shall sing,
The Snowdrop bringeth Hope and Spring.'

Thomas Miller

25

Sweet Violet

I think the King is but a man as I am:
The violet smells to him as it doth to me.

Shakespeare

MOST OF US can remember some bank on which the violet blows—some green lane or pleasant footpath where we have been stopping in spring by its fragrance. This modest flower was dear to the hearts of our Elizabethan poets; from its sweetness, buried amid the broad green leaves, they drew forth many an exquisite image. Shakespeare mentions it in his plays on no less than eighteen different occasions, and Sir Francis Bacon, in his writings, regarded the violet as possessing the sweetest scent of all flowers.

The violet's history goes back long before the birth of Christ to ancient Greece where the flowers were cultivated for their perfume and sweetening qualities, and held in such high esteem they became the emblem of the city of Athens.

The flower was also held in equally high regard in France since earliest times. It had much publicity through being a favourite of Napoleon who always gave a bouquet of violets to Josephine on their wedding anniversary. When she died, in 1814, he covered her grave with violet plants. When Napoleon was on his way to exile in Elba, he promised his supporters to 'return with the violets in the spring', which he did, on 20 March 1815. The flower was immediately adopted by his supporters as their symbol, and 'Caporal Violet' became their favourite toast. After his death, the flowers picked from his beloved Josephine's grave were found in a locket he had always worn around his neck.

Violets have been admired, smelt, and eaten through the ages. The blooms were used for strewing on the floors of all houses, from mansions to humble cottages, for overpowering damp, musty smells, and were prized as perfume to disguise the unsavoury smells of unwashed bodies and clothes.

Perfumes were never richer, more elaborate, costly or more delicate than in the time of Queen Elizabeth I, who spent extravagantly on them. Queen Victoria loved violets too, and always wore a posy for daytime and evening wear—for love of the flowers themselves, not for the sweetening powers of their perfume as in the Elizabethan days. Over 4,000 violet plants were grown under frames at Windsor Castle to provide the Queen and her ladies-in-waiting with a constant supply. Violets were also the favourite flowers of

'Buy my sweet violets.'

Queen Alexandra (married to Queen Victoria's eldest son Edward VII). She was seldom without a bouquet of them.

Violets have been dried and crystallized in England for eating as sweets and on cakes since mediaeval times, as well as being cooked with meat and game, or eaten raw in salads.

'Buy my sweet violets—a penny a bunch' was one of the familiar cries of old London. During the 1850s almost a million bunches of cut flowers were sold yearly in the streets. Sweet violets accounted for around 65,000 bunches; the flower-sellers paid one shilling for a dozen bunches—mostly from Covent Garden. They were able to make up three bunches from every two and make sixpence a day, including Sundays, unless the weather was bad when they couldn't sell any flowers at all.

Strewing, Perfumes, Pomanders, Pot-Pourri

> A certain lord, neat, and trimly dress'd,
> Fresh as a bridegroom, and his chin new reap'd
> Show'd like a stubble-land at harvest-home.
> He was perfumed like a milliner,
> And 'twixt his finger and his thumb he held
> A pouncet-box, which ever and anon
> He gave his nose and took't away again.
>
> *Shakespeare*

DURING ELIZABETHAN TIMES men had as much need of perfume as the ladies. Baths were seldom taken and clothes rarely laundered. If it hadn't been for the fragrance of the flowers and herbs, which were collected and used in every conceivable way, it is doubtful if courtiers would have been so courteous, or writers so poetic. As it was, England had much to be thankful for during one of the most successful reigns in her history.

The queen loved fine clothes and was said to have 1,000 dresses in her wardrobe, all richly embroidered and finely decorated with jewels, and she also spent considerable sums on perfumes, as well as on the wages of her perfumers within the Court. When Edward, Earl of Oxford, presented her with a beautiful pair of perfumed and embroidered gloves she was so pleased with them that she sat for her portrait with them on her hands.

Another present which she appreciated consisted of a number of pomanders strung together which could be worn around the neck, or waist, in which a carefully selected mixture of flower petals, herbs, spices and other aromatic substances were contained. Gentlemen carried pomanders, too, as can be seen in portraits of those times, as well as the pouncet-box, with its perforated lid, mentioned by Shakespeare.

The mansions themselves and musty smells of apartments needed to be perfumed, too. In ancient Rome the streets were frequently strewed with roses during public rejoicings. The Elizabethans adopted the idea indoors and sprinkled rose water on the floors but, above all, they made sure that a plentiful supply of fragrant flowers, herbs, rushes and leaves were always available from the gardens for strewing on the floors. One of the most popular strewing plants was the sweet flag. The flowers, themselves, have an unpleasant smell, although when the leaves and stems are crushed and trodden upon they release a pleasant and refreshing scent. May (hawthorn) blossom was also popular, as well as balm and water mint. Meadowsweet was a particular favourite of Queen Elizabeth for strewing on the floors of her personal apartments.

Muslin bags, containing rose-buds and loose petals, were used to impart a sweet perfume to clothes in drawers, cupboards and wardrobes; bedrooms and other rooms were freshened with pot-pourris. Wooden or china bowls contained the dried leaves and petals of wild herbs and flowers, as well as cultivated ones such as rose petals, balm, bergamot, rosemary, thyme, marjoram, geranium, bay leaves, honeysuckle, lavender and verbena. Pot-pourris in open bowls not only give off a lovely smell, they also look attractive and both they, and the enclosed pomanders with their perforated holes are extremely popular today. Some of the most famous, which are bought in great numbers by tourists and visitors to England, are made to secret recipes 300 years old. The containers are fashioned in materials from ceramics to silver, or gold. Sir Walter Raleigh is said to have had pot-pourris in his rooms.

Another refinement of the times, which continued into the present century, was the use of finger bowls on the dining table which contained rose water for freshening and perfuming the hands.

When Queen Elizabeth died, the population of London was believed to be around 200,000. Just over sixty years later, in 1665, the Great Plague of London killed almost half that number. The plant, angelica, was said to have been effective as a medicine during an epidemic of plague in Milan a century and a half earlier. The leaves of the bay laurel or sweet bay were also said to counteract plagues. Hence the origin of the expression 'keeping at bay'. The use of plants to ward off germs had the backing of the medical profession but they could have little effect in the narrow, dirty streets of London, with open drains and closely-packed houses overrun with rats.

When the Great Fire of London destroyed over 13,000 houses and 90 churches in 1666, the year after the Plague, although few people were killed, there were many who considered it a blessing in disguise as they believed that the fire had cleansed London of all traces of the plague. No doubt it helped, but the real cause of the plague were the black rats, which arrived in ships from countries where the plague was common. Fortunately, another rat—the brown rat—attacked and killed the black ones. But two centuries passed before the true cause of the plague was discovered to come from the fleas of the black rats which carried the germs of the dreaded disease.

A rebuilt, cleaner, London, with houses of brick and stone instead of wood, and metal discs placed on the mooring ropes of ships at the docks to prevent rats from coming ashore, became a safer and more pleasant place.

Tulips

DURING THE 1630s this flower created a sensation at which we may well imagine violets, daisies, and all quiet flowers were much amazed. The love of tulips became a mania and it was no rare thing to see a family ruined

Tulips.

through the father's overwhelming passion for cultivating rare bulbs.

The Dutch were the first to become obsessed with the craze paying such high prices for single bulbs, as much as £1,314 in some cases, that laws had to be introduced limiting the price to £400 (or approximately 960 dollars).

Tulipomania, in which the striped and feathered tulips were the most highly sought after, lasted for seven years with fortunes being won and lost—often in unexpected ways. On one occasion, a sailor waiting in the office of a Dutch merchant ate a bulb which he saw resting on the desk, imagining it to be an onion. Cooks made similar mistakes and one bulb farmer found out, too late, that he had just eaten a stew of his rarest tulip bulbs costing over £7,000.

They were certainly edible, for the seventeenth century gardener John Parkinson preserved some in sugar and found them very pleasant '... fit to be presented to the curious'. The bulbs were also used as food in Holland during World War 2.

No mention of tulips appears to have been made in ancient literature. They are on record, however, as being first introduced into England from Turkey by way of Vienna, in about 1578, during the reign of Queen Elizabeth I. New specimens were much sought after and still costly in 1854

when the catalogue of a Clapham nurseryman offered a few varieties at a hundred guineas each. Prices did not drop to those amateur gardeners could afford until the end of Queen Victoria's reign.

The wild tulip, with its fragrant yellow flowers and narrower leaves, was the only variety to become naturalized and is the symbol of hopeless love.

The Cottage Garden

LITTLE DID THE proud courtiers and stately dames of Queen Elizabeth I dream that the sweet-scented White Jasmine creeper (a sprig of which seemed to make the haughty, haughtier still) would one day become so common as to cluster around, and embower, thousands of humble English cottages. A degradation, which could they have but witnessed, would almost have made every plait of their starched ruffles bristle up, like 'quills on the fretful porcupine'.

In the language of flowers white jasmine is the emblem of amiability. Its sweetness, beauty, and star-like flowers, bear about them a resemblance to an amiable lady.

Its red buds, and white galaxy of flowers, which bloom from June until September, garland many a happy home. It is believed to have been introduced into England from Asia round about the middle of the 16th century, and is the jasmine used in perfumes.

The Yellow Jasmine has practically no scent but it adorns many cottage gardens as it will grow almost anywhere and provide cheer during the long dark days of winter with its generous display of golden flowers from November right though until the spring. The Winter Jasmine was introduced from China by Robert Fortune in 1844, and considered a pearl of great price, although it could be bought for a shilling. It has remained popular through the years and Yellow Jessamine has been adopted as the state flower of South Carolina.

The bonny Broom is one of England's oldest cottage and country flowers, and was as familiar to the eye of the ancient Briton as it is to our own. Neither has its name undergone any change, for Alfred the Great called it the broom, as we do now.

When Geoffrey, prince of Anjou and Maine, went on a pilgrimage to the Holy Land, he replaced the feather in his helmet with a sprig of yellow broom. Its Latin name was *Planta genista* and so it came about that, as father of England's Henry II, the royal name of Plantagenet came to be adopted.

Sprigs of broom were often given at weddings for, as there are so many little flowers on each stem, it was thought that it would act as a fertility charm and the couple would be blessed with a large family.

The broom is also the emblem of humility and neatness—the twigs having been used for sweeping cottages and homes since the Middle Ages. Its quality of neatness prompted Miss S. C. Edgarton to write this poem published in 1851:

> I love to see thy gentle hand
>   Dispose, with modest grace,
> The household things around thy home,
>   And 'each thing in its place'.
>
> And then thy own trim, modest form,
>   Is always neatly clad;
> Thou sure wilt make the tidiest wife
>   That ever husband had!
>
> No costly splendours needest thou
>   To make thy home look bright;
> For neatness on the humblest spot,
>   Can shed a sunny light.'

Hollyhocks are another noble English cottage garden occupant. A native of Syria, the hollyhock is believed to have been the Holy Mallow discovered by the Crusaders and brought by them to Europe. Its history of cultivation in Britain is believed to go back more than 500 years.

Legends also associate Geraniums with the mallow. The prophet Muhammad is said to have washed his shirt and hung it up to dry on a mallow plant. On returning to retrieve the garment, the humble mallow had been transformed into a magnificent geranium.

The geranium was brought to England originally from South Africa in the 17th century and grew in popularity through the plant's variously coloured flowers. The leaves of certain varieties, when given a gentle rub, release beautiful scents, ranging from almond and roses through to lemon and nutmeg. Much prized as a bedding plant, they were to be found in almost every garden by Victorian times.

Although Gladioli are sun-lovers, coming from South and Central Africa, they manage to thrive in English gardens and enrich them with their many splendid colours.

Delphiniums, both single and double, are also mangnificent, and available in a wide variety today. Their history of cultivation goes back to the time of the Pharaohs. In England they were known as Larkspur and were cultivated

The cottage garden.

in gardens in Elizabethan times. The name delphinium comes from the Greek *delphinion* which is derived from the word *delphis*—a dolphin—whose head the flower buds were thought to resemble.

Associations between mammals, birds, and other creatures and their resemblance to flowers appear frequently. Aquilegia, also known as 'columbine' or 'granny bonnet', is another such old-fashioned garden flower. The botanical name *aquila* is Latin for eagle, and *columba* means a dove. Both names provide a fanciful resemblance to this bird-like flower which has been a favourite in English cottage gardens for centuries. Columbine is the state flower of Colorado, and some of the long-spurred varieties grown today in English gardens were introduced over a hundred years ago, from the USA.

There are many legends about the Fuchsia, native of Central and South America, and New Zealand. It is the symbol of 'Taste'. One story attributes its introduction into Britain to a sailor who brought the plant home from Chile in the late 18th century and gave it to his wife (his mother, in some accounts). The plant bore flowers of a kind unknown till then in Europe. In time James Lee, an eminent nurseryman of Hammersmith, saw the plant in the window of the cottage at Wapping, in London's dockland, and offered a handsome sum for it. The bargaining continued until the sum offered reached 80 guineas then, and only then, did the lady agree to sell it providing he promised to give her a rooted cutting. Mr Lee returned to Hammersmith and eventually procured from its cuttings several hundred plants. Instead of one healthy specimen, he gave her three, and sold the rest.

From these and other specimens brought principally from Central and South America came the plants whose brilliant, drooping, funnel-shaped blossoms of fine colourings, graced the old-fashioned gardens. The greatest sensation experienced by the floral world in connection with the fuchsia, however, came some fifty years later when Messrs Veitch obtained the first flowering plants of yet another species of fuchsia from seeds sent home by William Lobb, who discovered it in Peru growing in the Andes at an elevation of 4,000 to 5,000 feet.

The fuchsia, also known as 'Lady's Eardrops', is beyond doubt one of the most beautiful of garden flowers. Shirley Hibberd, who wrote much of interest about flowers towards the end of the last century, summed up the beauty of the fuchsia with this story: 'A lean curé dined with a fat bishop, who first gave the curé a very poor *vin ordinaire*. But the curé praised the miserable wine, and astonished the bishop, who now determined to astonish the curé. So he brought forth his wines of rare vintage, and watched for the effect, but the curé spoke not a word. "What," said the bishop, "you praise my meagre *vin ordinaire*, and you say nothing of the wine now before you!"

'"Pardon, monsignor," replied the curé, "the wretched wine you first gave me needed praising; but this—this speaks for itself."' As regards the elegance and freshness of the Fuchsia 'it is not needful to speak', wrote Shirley Hibberd. *'It speaks for itself!'*

No type of flower garden is more delightful than the old-fashioned garden. Every garden needs to be created and everyone knows the satisfaction to be gained through growing things.

> One is nearer God's Heart in a garden
> Than anywhere else on earth.

Dorothy Gurney

A great deal of enjoyment is obtained from watching the opening and closing of flowers. Some do it so quickly that you can actually see their petals move. Linnaeus (1707–1778), the world-famous Swedish botanist, noted that plants opened and closed at specific times of the day or night and listed plants from which a twenty-four hour 'floral clock' could be made in gardens.

Goat's Beard was one of the plants included in Linnaeus' floral clock. The alternative name of this plant— 'Jack-go-to-bed-at-noon'—was used commonly because the flowers open early in the morning and close at noon.

The Star of Bethlehem, with its white star-like flowers, doesn't open until the middle of the morning, hence its other name of 'Ten o'clock Lady', by which it is known in England and America. It closes again at three.

The Scarlet Pimpernel awakens earlier at 8 a.m., but also closes about 3 p.m. Its many local names include 'Shepherd's Clock', 'Shepherd's Sundial' and 'Shepherd's Watch'. While the 'Flower of an Hour', which is a kind of mallow, got its name through remaining open only between 8 a.m. and 9 a.m.

The Blue Convolvulus, or 'Morning Glory', which we see so commonly twined around porches and beneath window-sills, constantly closes its flowers about four o'clock, and such a regular 'go-to-bed', as it is called in the country, is no bad emblem of repose.

Some of the timings in the old dial of flowers lists were precise, with minutes detailed. The Common Dandelion, for instance, was said to open at six minutes past five and close at nine minutes past eight. Children usually prefered to tell the time by blowing on the seed-head of the dandelion—the number of puffs needed indicating the time, or hour of the day. The dandelion has long been known as 'the Clock Flower', 'Farmer's Clocks', 'Time-Teller' or 'What o' Clock'.

It is not surprising that the flowers were used in this way, for the first pocket-watches, invented in Germany, were not available in England until 1577, during the reign of Elizabeth I. Some time before that, Charles V, the Holy Roman Emperor, had exclaimed, 'What an egregious fool must I have been to have squandered so much blood and treasure in an absurd attempt to make all men think alike, when I cannot even make a few watches keep time together!'

King Alfred the Great had used candles, painted with bands of different breadths and colours, to tell the time and know when he had been employed long enough about any one thing. This clever idea did not quite answer his purpose for he found when the wind blew upon them they burnt quicker and he had to contrive lanterns to put them in.

The ancient Babylonians were the first to measure time by making sundials. The Greeks also used them and it remained the most general time-measuring device until the invention of clocks. Sundials are still an attractive feature of gardens today. Just as the sun's position indicated the time on the dials, so too did it influence the opening and closing of the flowers.

THE FLOWER-DIAL

Twas a lovely thought to mark the hours
  As they floated in light away,
By the opening and the folding flowers,
  That laugh to the summer's day.

Thus had each moment its own rich hue,
  And its graceful cup and bell,
In whose coloured vase might sleep the dew,
  Like the pearl in an ocean-shell.

To such sweet signs might the time have flowed
  In a golden current on,
Ere from the garden, man's first abode,
  The glorious guests were gone.

So might the days have been brightly told—
  Those days of songs and dreams,—
When shepherds gathered their flocks of old
  By the blue Arcadian streams.

Fuchsias or 'Lady's Eardrops'.

So in those isles of delight, that rest
    Far off in a breezeless main,
Which many a bark, with a weary guest,
    Has sought, but still in vain.

Yet is not life, in its real flight,
    Marked thus—even thus—on earth,
By the closing of one hope's delight,
    And another's gentle birth?

Oh! let us live, so that flower by flower,
    Shutting in turn, may leave
A lingerer still for the sun-set-hour—
    A charm for the shaded eve.

Felicia Dorothea Hemans

Gardens have their night side, as well as their day side, and some flowers remain closed until twilight and then open to receive the night-flying insects which they need. These are usually pure white, or light-coloured flowers, often relying on their strong scents to attract the insects which seek them.

The star-white jasmine is one of the sweet perfumers of the night, which only throws out its full fragrance when its sister stars are keeping watch in the sky.

Apart from the fragrance of the flowers, and flight of the moths as they journey to and fro, an old-world garden is one of the most peaceful and relaxing places of all to hear the song birds at their best. The nightingale, for example, after its arrival from Africa, though it does sing during the day, is heard with louder and purer notes and fewer pauses through the night, when most of the other birds are resting or asleep.

For a final touch of magic in the surrounding darkness there is the light from the glow-worm, as she signals to her mate. The bluish-green light is produced in both male and female by a chemical process, though the light of the male is not so luminous. The female has no wings and relies on the more fortunately equipped male to fly towards her. Glow-worm larvae eat slugs and snails which makes this beetle, with its shining beacon, not only one of nature's miracles but also the gardener's friend.

In former times the occupants of the old cottages in use today relied upon soft rush which was used for lights and the wicks of candles. If ever the clock turns back and we run out of fuel and natural energy resources, the writings of Gilbert White (1720–1793), English country parson, naturalist and author, give instructions in *The Natural History of Selborne* on how five and a half hours lighting could be obtained for a farthing!

Bluebells—Hyacinths

THE BLUEBELL is the earliest spring flower that bears old England's favourite blue. It is the universal favourite of both old and young that lights up the darkness of the forest and looks as if a blue cloud had fallen from the face of heaven, and was sleeping there. A vast carpet of bluebells usually indicates that their woodland home has been there for many centuries.

Bluebell flowers are very like hyacinths grown in gardens and the early botanists classified the plant as the hyacinth, although, subsequently, we are informed that we should not call the bluebell the wild hyacinth, but they still do so in Scotland. However the bluebells of Scotland are known as harebells in England, which is all very confusing. To complicate things further, bluebells, which have a strong sweet smell, can also be pink or white. For refreshment, not clarity, we need to turn to four lines from one of the great English poets:

> And the hyacinth—purple, white and blue,
> Which flung from its bells a sweet peal anew
> Of music so delicate, soft and intense,
> It was felt like an odour within the sense.

> *Shelley*

Bowls of hyacinths are welcome guests in any home with their delightful fragrance. Madame de Pompadour can be said to have started the custom and enhanced the hyacinth's popularity when she ordered the French Court to cultivate them indoors during the winter months.

As one might imagine, the Dutch made use of their great skills in propagating hyacinths and raised the first double one. Others followed, which caught the public fancy, and started a boom with bulbs of some of the more popular varieties selling for anything between the equivalent of £100 to £200 apiece by the mid-18th century. The Dutch Government intervened by warning people not to over speculate in them and, as a result, the prices paid for the love of the plant were prevented from reaching the heights of those during the 'tulipomania', just over a century earlier, when fortunes had been won and lost.

Pansies

> There is Pansies, that's for thoughts.

> *Shakespeare*

No flower has more names than the Pansy. There are at least three-score in England and more than three times that number in Europe. Shakespeare immortalized this flower, calling it 'Love-in-Idleness', while others have given it no end of endearing names such as 'Three-faces-under-a-hood', 'Jump-up-and-kiss-me', 'Kiss-me-at-the-garden-gate', and so on to 'Lover's Thoughts', 'Heartsease' and 'Eyebright'.

Most of the ancient legends about the pansy are lost except for the one woven into Shakespeare's inimitable *Midsummer Night's Dream*:

> The juice of it, on sleeping eyelids laid,
> Will make, a man or woman, madly dote
> Upon the next live creature that it sees.

Pansies.

No one who has read or seen this matchless play will forget the pleasing confusion it makes amongst the lovers in the wood. Oberon squeezes the juice of the pansy into Titania's eyes so that she falls in love with the ass-headed Bottom, when she awakes.

For another, lesser known, story about this flower we must turn to the adventurous days of King Arthur when his round table was never without a gallant guest, and the armed knights began to seek for signs in the secret virtues of the flowers. For, most of all, to the petals of the pansy did they turn their thoughts, and in its freaked flowers seek to learn their destiny. If the petal they plucked was pencilled with four lines, it signified hope. If from the centre line a branch started, when the streaks numbered five, it still meant hope—springing out of fear. When the lines were thickly branched, and leaned towards the left, they foretold a life of trouble; but if they bent towards the right, they were then supposed to denote prosperity unto the end. Seven streaks they interpreted as constancy in love, and if the centre one was longest, they prophesied that Sunday would be their wedding day. Eight denoted fickleness; nine a changing heart; and eleven, the most ominous of all, disappointment in love and an early grave.

The name for the original wild pansy came from the French word *pensée*, meaning thought, the noblest faculty with which mankind is gifted.

In the course of time the cultivated varieties have given us larger flowers, with rich and more brilliant colours from white, yellow and orange to dark brown. Others are pink, red, blue, violet, mauve and purple, sometimes with a mixture of three or so colours, all on the same flower.

Apple Blossom, Forsythia, Aubrietia

ONE OF THE MOST inspiring sights of gardens and the countryside each year comes with the arrival of the ornamental fruit tree blossoms, such as the apple, cherry, pear and plum. As we look at them we tend to forget that they all belong to the rose family—as do the peach, strawberry, raspberry, and many other fruits. But, if we look at the blossom of the apple and compare it with the wild rose blossom in the hedgerows, the resemblance soon becomes apparent.

No fruit has received more attention throughout the world than the apple which has featured in the literature of all ages. According to the Bible, we have been led to believe that the forbidden fruit, eaten by Adam and Eve in the Garden of Eden, was the apple. However, it could have been any one of many other fruits, for in Genesis we do not read specifically of the apple but of 'the fruit of the tree which is in the midst of the garden'.

The art of hospitality, according to a sage, lies 'in making people feel at home when you wish they were'. When a marriage was being celebrated by the Greek gods and goddesses, Eris, the goddess of Discord, was not invited, so she threw a 'golden apple' among the guests on which she had written 'For the Fairest'. An event which was to lead to inflamed jealousies and dire consequences. When things got out of control, Paris (the son of the king of Troy) was called upon to award the prize of beauty amongst three of the most determined contenders. The goddess Hera (Juno) and queen of the heaven tried to bribe him with promises of power and riches if he would select her. Athena (Minerva) topped that with the offer of glory and renown in war. Aphrodite (Venus), the goddess of love, flowers and fruitfulness, stole the show by whispering in his ear that if she were awarded the prize, she would give him the love of the most beautiful woman in the mortal world. Paris could not resist the offer and gave her the 'golden apple'. Perhaps this could explain why in the language of flowers, apple blossom has been chosen to represent 'preference'. Whenever someone wins, there have to be losers. Some take it well, others do not—from that moment the other two goddesses became the enemies of Paris and the city of Troy.

Aphrodite kept her promise and gave Paris the fairest of all earthly women—Helen—the beautiful wife of Menelaus, king of Sparta. When the king bade her to return, and she refused, he summoned all the princes of Greece to avenge the loss of his wife. This event was responsible for the ten year war which arose between the Trojans and the Greeks. Eventually the Greeks managed to capture and destroy the city by entering Troy in the famous wooden horse.

The story of Troy, recounted in Homer's epic poem, *The Iliad*, was long thought to be imaginery until 1870 when, thanks to an enterprising archaeologist, Heinrich Schliemann, the fiction was proved to be fact. For, as he began to dig, it became apparent that he had discovered the very spot where the Trojan war had been waged. He, and the teams of archaeologists who followed after his death, discovered the ruins of nine towns built one upon the other during a period of highly developed civilization extending over 3,500 years. This task called for backbreaking, but patient, labour for 50 years until the last and earliest city, built around 3,000 B.C., was uncovered.

Fifty years before Schliemann started his excavations another important discovery had been made—the marble statue of the *Venus de Milo* which is still regarded as the most beautiful statue in the world. A widely held belief is that the goddess originally held an apple in her hand which was the symbol of the Greeek island of Melos (Milo) on which her statue was found buried amid the ruins. As the arms were broken off and missing, and have never been found, no one can be sure, although the theory seems more than likely to be true.

For the ancestor of all edible cultivated apples we need look no further than the wild crab apple. This tree is also a member of the Rose family and often lives for 50 years or so; many of the decorative forms grown in our gardens for their colourful and attractive blossoms and foliage are derived from it.

In Britain, most of the ornamental trees are derived either from native crab apple species, or from those introduced from Siberia, China and Japan, or North America.

Apple blossom has been adopted as the state flower of both Arkansas, and Michigan.

Another springtime blossom, welcomed in gardens everywhere, is Forsythia, with its branches of golden-yellow flowers. It was named after William Forsyth, gardener to George III, in charge of the gardens at both Kensington and St James's Palaces, and one of the seven founder members of the Royal Horticultural Society at a meeting in Hatchard's Bookshop in Piccadilly, London in 1804. He was an influential man who also spent more than a dozen years as curator of the Physic Garden at Chelsea where he made many alterations and additions, including the construction of one of the

Apple blossom, forsythia, aubrietia.

earliest rock gardens, built with stones from the Tower of London and lava from Iceland.

Forsyth also made an attempt to solve one of the major problems facing England at the time, concerning the oak. No tree has figured more prominently throughout history than the mighty oak, which has more than once affected the destiny of England. Oak was the ideal material for building ships, but wholesale felling of these trees in the forests throughout the 17th century resulted in a shortage of timber. The trees that were left at the beginning of the 18th century were either too old or decayed.

According to a report made for the House of Commons in the 1790s, 2,000 oak trees of 75 years' growth were required to build a 74-gun ship, with another 1,000 mature oaks being necessary to build a larger man o' war. The average life of an oak tree is 250 years, though some live for 1,000 years or more. But oaks are in the highest perfection for timber when from 75 to 100, or at most 150 years old. The first age is that in which the oak trees were usually cut down for shipbuilding.

Forsyth's answer to stop the decay affecting the oak trees which made them unsuitable for shipbuilding was to produce a 'plaister' which he claimed would render the trees 'as fit for the navy as though they never had been injured'. It was considered of such importance by the authorities that Parliament formed a joint commission to investigate his claims. If satisfied that it was effective, they promised to give him an immediate award of £1,500, with the promise of more as the plaister was put into use.

The Commission was satisfied, and Forsyth got his money and published the details of his secret formula in the *London Gazette*. When Forsyth died shortly afterwards, in 1804, the year before Trafalgar, bitter controversy arose amongst the country's leading gardeners as to the effectiveness of the plaister, or, more accurately, a complete lack of it for, in their opinion, it was useless.

Sadly, Forsyth tends to be remembered for this rather than for the major contributions he made towards the art of gardening and advance of horticulture. It is worth noting, however, that in modern times many inventions which have been deemed useless by the 'experts' have, eventually when allowed to, been effective and saved the nation. Also that many products today, work well when used correctly, and not at all when applied or used incorrectly. A good product in expert hands can work wonders, whereas a good product in inexpert hands can prove useless. Had Forsyth lived a little longer and been able to bring his instruction and experience to bear on the application of the plaister, the result might well have been different and silenced his critics. No doubt adjustments might have been necessary when applying it to the trees in the forests but his product had been put up to official scrutiny, and come out well. For critics, no doubt jealous ones, to claim after his death that his product was worthless seems totally unjust. It is they that we should forget, and the pioneer gardener William Forsyth whom we should remember. It is through the shrub named after him, which we grow today, that we are able to do just that!

One thing about which everyone is agreed, whether they live in Britain or come as visitors from across the world's oceans, is the beauty of the villages set throughout the length and breadth of the countryside. Each one has its own character, built from local materials ranging from flint and stone to local timber, which today has a tale to tell of days that have been and evokes a nostalgia for more peaceful and leisurely times.

Somehow villages, unlike busy and noisy towns, bring hope even on the wettest and drabbest of days. Country dwellers have always taken pride in their own villages, and if reassurance is needed that villages will always be there, come what may, there are the plants, foliage and flowers to inspire us. Amongst them is aubrietia, providing a mass of colour in many shades of blue, mauve, purple and crimson, which grows amidst stones and over walls in seemingly impossible conditions, asking little but giving much.

Anemones and pasque flowers with Easter eggs.

Anemone and Pasque Flower

MANY LEGENDS have been woven around the Anemone, one of the most beautiful of all spring blossoms, which always seem to be moving and shaking in the wind. Its name comes from the Greek word *anemos*, meaning wind, which accounts for the alternative name of 'wind flower'.

The flower is said to have sprung up from the blood of Christ, at the foot of the Cross. In another story, during the Crusades, Bishop Umberto of Pisa ordered the seamen carrying soldiers to the Holy Land to bring back soil, instead of sand, as ballast in their empty ships. When this was spread over the Campo Sancto at Pisa, to honour and bury the dead, the next spring the sacred soil became covered with a blaze of scarlet anemones. It was a miracle, as if they had sprung from the blood of martyrs, and from then on pilgrims carried the plants and seeds all over Europe.

In its wild form in woods and pastures, the flowers of the Wood Anemone vary from white and pink, sometimes yellow, a reddish-purple or even blue. The flowers droop gracefully in the evening, or when it rains. The cultivated varieties are grown and treasured all over the world and, in some instances, the early enthusiasts went to considerable lengths to acquire them.

During the early 17th century, a certain French florist obtained some fine specimens from the Far East, which he refused to part with or even sell. Ten years passed without anyone being able to persuade him to change his mind, until a gentleman of high rank visited the garden. On this visit his cloak slipped on to the border where the precious flowers were growing. His coachman, acting on cue, gathered and rolled up the 'offending' garment and took it back to the carriage. Then, in time, the fluffy seeds which had attached themselves came to grow profusely in the cloak-owner's garden, from which plants were distributed to friends all over Europe.

The West became indebted to the botanist Robert Fortune for another exotic species, the Japanese anemone, which he brought back to England in plant form from China almost halfway through the 19th century. His official report, which he described as a 'long but favourable voyage' made light of his adventures.

The Chinese made great use of plants for the decoration of their cemeteries, using simple but beautiful flowers, and it was among the graves of Shanghai that Fortune set out alone to look for the Japanese anemone. It suddenly became apparent that several Chinese gathered there were advancing menacingly towards him to rob, or perhaps to kill him. Using attack as the best form of defence he lashed out and managed to send some tumbling down a slope. As others tried to pull him down he struggled free and made a dash for the exit. As those outside tried to bolt it, Fortune threw himself against the door, bursting it open and sending them flying. Seizing his chance in the disarray, he took flight, running as fast as he could despite injury from a flying brick hurled at him, and finally made his escape.

Within two years he was off to China again, enthusiastic as ever, collecting valuable new plants which eventually found their way into our gardens, followed, some years later, by yet another plant expedition, this time to Japan.

The Pasque Flower, which is considered one of Britain's most exotic and beautiful wild flowers, takes its name from *Paques*, the French word for Easter, because it comes out traditionally at this time. This purple anemone was thought to grow where blood had been spilt; one of the oldest Easter customs was the exchanging of coloured eggs as symbols of continuing life and resurrection. The colours varied but originally were red to commemorate the blood of Christ, shed for us on Good Friday.

In later years Edward I, who next to Alfred was one of the greatest kings to occupy the English throne, spent eighteen pence (in 1290) on the purchase of 450 eggs which were to be dyed and gilded for distribution amongst the royal household, and the pasque flower petals were among the plants used for colouring.

It was a custom for Easter eggs to be blessed in church by the parish priest and Pope Pius V composed a form of blessing to be used in Britain and Ireland.

Today, eggs are still decorated in many different countries, followed by individual customs and ceremonies. Some of the favourite games played with the eggs in Britain and European countries included throwing them in the air and then catching them. When an egg was dropped, a penalty had to be paid. In another game the child who won had taken the trouble to boil their coloured eggs really hard. For, like the traditional game of 'conkers', opponents eggs were struck by hitting them with a hard-boiled egg held firmly in the hand giving a sharp blow at arm's length. Those unfortunate enough to break their egg had to give it to the victor.

Coloured hard-boiled eggs used to be rolled down slopes, and still are in some countries, the winner being the person whose egg remained intact longest—or the one that was less damaged than others. Most of the games were just for fun, though others were more sophisticated, attracting large entries and spectators. In America, today, around 100,000 eggs are still rolled each year at Easter on the White House lawns. The custom does not appear to have been taken up outside Washington, despite the fact that the pasque flower is the state flower of South Dakota.

Eggs have been regarded as symbols of continuing life and resurrection since ancient times, long before being linked with the Easter celebrations.

Anemones are believed to have been among the flowers growing in the Holy Land and, according to one legend, the Virgin Mary coloured eggs to amuse the baby Jesus.

The pasque flower has now become very rare in the British countryside through being over-picked, but it has been cultivated in gardens for 400 years and can be obtained from your nurseryman or garden centre. If seeds are purchased, do not be surprised when you open the packet at home. Many people imagine they have been off-loaded with a packet of cotton wool but they are in fact seeds which developed, once flowering was over, within the heads of the hairy fruits.

Primrose

> Aye, flowers! The very name of flowers,
> That bloom in wood and glen,
> Brings Spring to me in Winter's hours,
> And childhoods' dreams again.
> The Primrose on the woodlands lee
> Was more than gold and lands to me.
>
> *John Clare*

JOHN CLARE OBVIOUSLY LOVED the countryside and its flowery furnishings. But like many of us, if we had our time over again, he and we would arrange our lives differently—study nature more closely and thus enjoy life more. For in a letter to a friend he wrote: 'If life had a second edition, how I would correct the proofs.'

It is not easy to associate a flower as simple as the primrose with the next gentleman. This was someone who, early in his career, attired himself in such extremes of fashion as a black velvet coat lined with satin, a crimson waistcoat, green or mauve velvet trousers, and extravagantly jewelled rings worn outside his white gloves. The man was none other than Benjamin Disraeli (1804–1881) novelist and brilliant statesman, twice Prime Minister of Great Britain, created Earl of Beaconsfield—and the primrose was his favourite flower.

His speech and manner were as extrovert as his dress and when he was shouted down in the House of Commons, while attempting to speak for the first time, he agreed to sit down—but not before declaring that 'the time is coming when you will hear me.' And hear him they did, for after working

Lupins and gladioli.

hard to make his prophesy come true, changing his mode of dress and ways, his speeches were listened to attentively. The debates between him and his rival Gladstone, the leader of the Liberal party, were among the finest ever heard in the House.

Just as the primrose was Disraeli's favourite flower, he was Queen Victoria's favourite Prime Minister. When he died, primroses were sent from Osborne House—her royal residence on the Isle of Wight—to form a wreath placed on his coffin; a card was attached on which 'His favourite flower' was written in her own hand.

Within two years the Conservatives had founded The Primrose League to cherish his ideals and memory. Primrose Day on 19 April, the anniversary of his death, was from then on always celebrated by the wearing of this flower.

This favourite of pleasantly scented flowers, both wild and in the garden, is conveniently in bloom over Easter and is therefore much used in church decorations at this festival.

Primroses had another charming use. In the past it was customary for servants working away from home to be given a holiday during mid-Lent. As they walked along the lanes to the station, frequently a long walk, they gathered primroses and other wild flowers as a present for their mother on

Mothering Sunday. This custom continued in its original form until the end of the 19th century before being revived and commercialised in more recent years.

In our modern world, from the comfort of our armchairs, we have been able to see what the surface of the moon, and distant planets, look like. They have no green grass, nor galaxy of flowers. When we think of them it can only serve to remind us how lucky we are here on Earth.

In bygone days the magic of primroses was used to reveal sites where treasure was concealed. Just how, we are not told, which is just as well as primroses, like many other wild flowers, are becoming rarer and should be left where they they are—treasures in themselves—so that others may enjoy them as well as ourselves.

Tea and Camellias

THE CAMELLIA, which is one of the most beautiful flowers ever introduced into Britain, belongs to the family that provides us with our tea. It is a native of China and Japan, named in honour of Georg Josef Kamel (1661–1706)—a Jesuit monk and botanist of considerable fame. Whether he actually brought seeds back with him to Europe is not certain. The Camellia Japonica was certainly introduced to Britain by Lord Petre in 1739, but the first plants were killed by kindness through being placed in too high a temperature and turned out to be much hardier than was at first imagined. In its natural environment, in mountain regions, it frequently grows to 30 ft (9 m) or so, though rarely over $6\frac{1}{2}$ ft (2 m) when cultivated.

The relative of the bright, hardy camellias, which bring pleasure and perfection to our gardens, known as the tea plant, has been growing in China since prehistoric times. Its use as a beverage, however, is said to have come about accidentally when a Buddhist dropped some leaves of the plant, from the branches he was using for a fire, into a pot of water he was boiling. When something prompted him to taste the liquid a little while later he found it most pleasant and refreshing. His discovery lead, through the centuries, to it becoming the favourite beverage of half the world's population.

The Dutch were the first to bring tea to Europe early in the 17th century. North America received it a year or two before Britain—the first tea-house being opened in London in 1657. The price was high and at sixty shillings (£3) a pound it was, at first, only within reach of the well-to-do. Extravagant claims were made by Thomas Garraway, the proprietor, for the beverage which was claimed to cure almost every conceivable malady anyone could possibly suffer from. Somewhat similar medicinal claims had also been made

Camellias.

in France but, despite controversy in medical circles, the beverage soon attained great popularity.

Samuel Pepys extolled the virtues of his first cup of tea in 1660 . . . but the most famous tea drinker of all must surely be Dr Samuel Johnson (1709–1784) who 'with tea amused the evening, with tea solaced the midnight—and with tea welcomed the morning'. His teapot held half a gallon and it was not unknown for him to drink twenty-five cups at a sitting.

Amongst the early claims for the beverage were that it prevented paralysis and dispelled vapours and giddiness. With Johnson as an advocate, who would dispute the fact that it stimulated mental activity? For this son of a bookseller, who spent all his childhood among books and later failed as a schoolmaster, went on to write the *Dictionary* which brought him such fame, after eight years of unremitting toil, that the degree (LL.D.) 'Doctor of Laws' was conferred upon him by the University of Oxford. Another honour was bestowed upon his memory when he died and was buried in Westminster Abbey.

During Dr Johnson's time, although tea was still highly priced, tea-drinking spread throughout the land, even into the humblest of homes. At first, few knew why this was: it was then discovered that more than half the tea consumed was being smuggled into the country by British and foreign merchantmen who were unloading their cargoes from mainland Europe in countless bays and coves around the British coast. Every resource of Government, and a considerable passage of time, was needed before this smuggling of tea could be plugged.

Dr Johnson could not have envisaged the speed at which cargoes of tea were to be raced across the world's oceans from the Far East to Europe and America, as the sailing ships were evolved into the tall tea Clippers during intense rivalry between the American and British shipbuilders in the quest for fast, and still faster, ships. Though, no doubt, he would have approved and been just as excited as everyone else had it happened in his lifetime. He knew the fast schooners and brigs — the Baltimore clippers — and it was from these, with the finer hull designs and strengthening of masts and spars to carry a greater sail area, that the famous tea clippers emerged.

This most romantic development in the history of sailing took place during the time of another great man, and champion of tea, who was also buried in Westminster Abbey. William Ewart Gladstone (1809–1898) — the 'Grand Old Man' of British Politics, member of Parliament for 60 years and Prime Minister on four different occasions — took a stone hot-water bottle to his bed not only to stem outer cold, but for inner warmth during the night through repeated drinks from its contents filled with tea.

During the great Clipper races of the mid-1800s a handsome prize was offered to the first ship to land their tea cargo from China at the London Docks. Excitement was intense, not only among the merchantmen, but also among the general public, and money wagered was on which of the six to eight ships would be the first to arrive. Suspense was heightened through a complete lack of news of their progress once they had left the Canton river until they were sighted in the English Channel. Despite the thousands of miles covered, quite often only ten minutes elapsed between the sighting of one vessel and another. The race was not over, though, until the first cargo was unloaded and this could not be done until the wind was in the right direction to assist the passage of the clippers up the River Thames.

Wind-clocks were mounted on the walls of tea merchants' offices, connected to a weather-vane, with a clerk on duty throughout the day and night, watching for the swing of the needle to the desired compass heading and favourable wind direction. If this happened during the night the clerk would rush to his waiting horse and gallop off to the home of his merchant, shouting the news to all and sundry as he passed, and those who happened to be awake in their beds. As the first Clipper docked, the victorious captain and crew received a tremendous ovation from the large crowd gathered, plus a bonus of around £500, or so, for being the first to unload their cargo. After fifteen years this romantic age of the Clippers declined as the competition from steamships grew and they took over from sail.

The old Chinese name for the tea plant species of camellia was pronounced *cha*, hence the expression 'cup of cha' which, though popular in recent times, is anything but modern. The pronunciation of the name camellia, itself, has left itself wide open to mispronunciation through the ages. It should be Cam*ell*ia (or camel rather than eel—*mell* not *meel*).

The fame of the camellia has been kept alive during the last hundred years through one of Alexandre Dumas the younger's best-known plays *Camille*. The play, adapted from his novel *La Dame aux Camélias*, was banned at first by the censors until Napoleon III intervened, when it became an instant success, and, for long, the favourite rôle of the great French actress Sarah Bernhardt. The story was based around an actual girl, whom Dumas loved, who always carried a bouquet consisting entirely of camellias, because she was allergic to scented flowers. She died tragically when only twenty-two. This story subsequently inspired Verdi to write his famous opera *La Traviata*.

Camellias are the symbol of perfection. Many people obtain additional pleasure from them by floating blooms in bowls of water indoors, and on the surface of ponds in their gardens.

Hawthorn

Come lasses and lads, get leave of your dads,
And away to the Maypole hie,
For every he has got him a she,
And the fiddler's standing by.

Anonymous

NOTHING COULD BE MORE NATURAL than for so sweet-scented and common a blossom as Hawthorn, or May (called after one of the pleasantest months in the whole year), to have been selected as the image of hope! For there are few who cannot recall with delight the healthy fragrance which has cheered them while wandering between the green hedgerows of England. Few have beheld it without trusting that there are still better days in store.

The hawthorn has for long been considered to be a 'protecting plant'. At the time of the Crusades, knights seldom left for the Holy Land without first giving their ladies sprigs of hawthorn, entwined with pink ribbon, as an assurance that they would 'live in hope'. Sprigs of it were used at wedding feasts in ancient Greece, and in Rome, as tokens of prosperity and happiness and, later, in England and France it was placed in cradles as a protection for infants against ill health and evil. To ensure an abundant supply of milk, it was hung outside cowsheds, and, on houses, it was intended to protect against lightning.

One cannot think of hawthorn, with its pink-white blossoms and one of the most fragrant scents of the countryside, without recalling the old May Day festivals. These go back at least to Roman times, to the festival of Flora, the goddess of flowers.

In England, in the Middle Ages, our ancestors paid homage to spring, and went out with songs and music to 'bring home May'. They erected arbours of green branches, selected a beautiful maiden and crowned her Queen of the May. They placed her upon a throne of flowers, wreathed her brow with blossoms, and danced around her, and they hung the tall, tapering Maypole with gay garlands of variegated colours. Even kings and queens left their palaces, the proud baron rode out from under the dark-browed archway of his feudal castle, the fair lady deserted her bower, and the brave knight, with his plumes dancing in the wind, mounted on his prancing war-horse, rode beside the white palfrey of his lady-love. So they went forth, throwing their titles and dignities aside for once, to 'do observance to the May'. Through green winding lanes, and the bridle-paths of ancient forests, the merry cavalcade went on singing 'How sweet is flowery May!'

For reasons best known to themselves, the Puritans strongly denounced Maypoles and May dances, and they were also forbidden by Parliament. They returned into favour, however, with the Restoration under Charles II, known as the 'Merry Monarch'—one of the most amusing, popular and clever kings ever to occupy the throne.

Although May Day festivals, Maypoles and associated customs of this innocent old English holiday, are still retained in certain areas today, something of the flavour and gaiety of those earlier ceremonies can be gleaned from detailed records.

Imagine a clear, bright morning in spring. One of those mornings in which summer seems to have come forth before her time, as if to look upon her great garden the earth to see how her buds and blossoms are progressing. In the centre of the open village-green, towering above the aged elm, stands a Maypole, hung with gaudy garlands, in which flutter ribands of as many dyes as there are varied hues in the flowers amid which they are twined. At the foot of the Maypole is a rustic throne of trellis-work, covered with flowers and branches of hawthorn blossoms. On it is seated the Queen of the May, her brow crowned with a simple wreath of wild roses while, hand in

Hawthorn at Glastonbury.

hand, young men and village maidens form a circle around her, smiling as they time their feet to the music of an old-fashioned country dance.

At a distance stands the squire, surrounded by his family, his face beaming as he gazes upon the merry group before him and points proudly to his youngest daughter, who sits crowned the Queen of the May. (For ages past some high-born daughter of the hall has laid aside her dignity for the day, and condescended to preside over their May games. Many a proud beauty, who now sleeps in the dark vault beneath the chancel pavement, on which shines the morning sun, has—in the young bloom of her loveliness—left her ancestral hearth and mounted the flowery throne on the village green.) But never before has there stepped out, from that long gallery of departed beauties, one lovelier than she who now sits the crowned queen of the month of flowers, her face resembling that of a goddess immortalized in Greek sculpture. Around her ivory neck hangs a band of rosebuds, the warm marble of her arms ornamented with bracelets of flowers, and the belt which encircles her slender waist covered with bunches of hawthorn blossoms. She appears as the Goddess of Flowers, newly alighted upon the earth, ascending that throne to preside over her worshippers. In her hand she holds a sceptre, covered with the choicest flowers of spring and, as she raises or lowers it, so the dancers proceed or halt in a moment in the midst of their merriment.

A handsome-looking young gentleman stands gazing upon the scene, with his horse's bridle thrown negligently over his arm while he times the measure of the dance with the butt-end of his riding-whip upon the ground. The Queen of the May lowers her flowery sceptre and, stopping the dance, beckons one of the village maidens to approach, when, whispering something in her ear, she takes the band of rosebuds from her neck and places it in the hands of the dancer, who exchanges a few words with five of her fair companions, and throwing the wreath of roses around the young gentleman brings him prisoner before the Queen of the May.

Laughing, he kneels down and kisses the hand extended towards him, then takes his seat beside her on the throne of flowers. Once again the music sounds, and the light-footed dancers whirl round the dizzy maze, now joined by the jolly English squire who makes the earth shake beneath the tread of his heavy top-boots. As a few bottles of the choicest wine brought from the cellars of the hall, have the corks drawn by a servant in livery, the healths of the King and Queen of May are drunk, amid loud 'huzzas', by the happy villagers.

After another dance, in which the queen and her lover join, the squire and his family retire through the ancient iron gates of the lodge, being soon lost to view in the long avenue which leads to the hall, leaving the merry villagers to end their May-day game amongst themselves.

They elect a new May queen by cutting a quantity of sprigs from a rose bush, amid which only one bud is placed. This, together with the sprays which contain only leaves, is concealed in the palm of the hand, while the stalks or stems only are left visible. Then she who is fortunate enough to draw out the rose bud is proclaimed Queen of the May, and placed upon the flowery throne which her sovereign sister has just abdicated. Happy, not only because of her enthronement, but in the ancient belief that the May dews which she gathered that morning before sunrise to anoint and beautify her complexion will also bring her good fortune during the next twelve months. This custom, of gathering the early morning May dew, is still continued to this day by some country girls.

Although the hawthorn is regarded as a 'protecting plant', it was considered unlucky to bring the blossom indoors. Thomas à Becket, however, liked his hall at Canterbury to be strewn every day in the spring with fresh May blossom. For him it could be said, perhaps, that bringing hawthorn indoors turned out to be unlucky, considering the manner of his death.

Most people sometimes say things they don't really mean, and King Henry II was certainly no exception. He deeply regretted ever having suggested that Becket should be 'got rid of'. It was said to friends at dinner — not in earnest, but in a quick outburst of temper. But four of his knights had taken him seriously and, unknown to him, decided to do something about it. The assassination, over 800 years ago, shocked the whole Christian world. Almost immediately after Becket's murder, miracles became associated with his tomb — and for centuries pilgrims travelled from all over Europe just to pray at Saint Thomas Becket's shrine.

They came in groups, some came alone — many on foot, others on horses — Chaucer amongst them. The easy gallop at which the pilgrims rode to Canterbury were to give us the word *canter*. Chaucer's *Canterbury Tales* are some of the finest examples of English story-telling.

Today, pilgrims come in their millions from all over the world to look at the wonder and majesty of Canterbury Cathedral — as well as to reflect on the strange circumstances that brought about the tragic murder of Thomas à Becket. Amongst them, and others, are thousands who still believe it is unlucky to bring hawthorn blossom indoors.

Many flowers, including hawthorn, are to be seen in the wooden and stone carvings and sculptures of churches and cathedrals. The hawthorn itself is reputed to have been used for Christ's crown of thorns. The famous Glastonbury thorn which flowers twice a year, in May and on Christmas Day, is said to have sprung from the hawthorn stick thrust into the Somerset hill by Joseph of Arimathea, who arrived in A.D. 60 to preach the Gospel and found the first Christian church in England. As he leant on his staff in prayer, it took root immediately and flowered. The thorns which can be seen at Glastonbury today are cuttings from the original holy thorn which was cut down at the time of Cromwell.

Hedgerows

NOT SO LONG AGO it was possible for a squirrel to cross from county to county without touching the ground; this was when much of Britain was covered by continuous woodland, stretching for hundreds of miles. It is not only the woodlands which have become depleted by man but also the hedgerows, with up to 5,000 miles being removed each year.

Hedgerows are part of the British scene, something which foreign visitors admire but we tend to take too much for granted, perhaps. Banish them entirely from the landscape and what sort of countryside would we have? Hedgerows not only give a patchwork quilt beauty to the landscape, they serve a vital purpose. They control farm stock and provide shelter from the elements for crops and animals; they act as windbreaks to prevent soil erosion of valuable farmland; they provide homes for birds, insects, and other animals, which are not only a joy to watch but useful on the farms and in the countryside, playing their part in the delicate balance of nature. The banks of hedgerows and grass verges provide perfect sites for myriad flowers and plant life, without which our lives would be considerably less rich and certainly duller.

Britain has the Enclosure Acts of the 18th and early 19th centuries to thank for her hedgerows. In Anglo-Saxon times the 'open-field' system of farming was used; fields were divided with grass strips, each of which was one furrow long (or one eighth of a mile) hence the term 'furlong'. As populations grew, farming methods had to change to enable more food to be grown and the Enclosure Acts made farming more efficient by creating larger units which were managed by landlords. Methods of dividing the fields varied in different parts of the country. Drystone walls had already been in use and more were built in some areas, but the main innovation was the introduction of hedges of hawthorn, beech, hazel, and elm, planted and trimmed to render them stockproof.

In time, all manner of visitors crept into the hedges to thicken them. Bramble, bryony, holly, honeysuckle, dog rose, old man's beard and many more. The banks, ditches and grass verges encouraged many different flowers to use them as their habitat and to brighten them.

Dog rose.

By and large, hedges were favoured to enclose land as it was more economical to grow them than to build walls, though where stone was abundant locally it made sense to utilise it. Considerable skill was needed by the hedgers to build and maintain good thick hedgerows. Some hedges planted over 500 years ago are still in use today. Hedges can be dated, approximately, by checking the number of woody species in them. Studies, and old documents, reveal that on average one extra woody species appears in a 100 ft (30 m) stretch of hedge in each hundred years of its life.

During the last thirty years or so, the tendency has been to grub up the hedgerows that have enclosed small fields for centuries, to enable modern farm machinery to be used more efficiently over large areas of unobstructed land. Although today it is easier, with modern machinery, to cultivate and harvest much larger fields, the penalties of this 'progress', through loss of windbreaks, have led to erosion of vital topsoil, and the depletion of suitable habitat for a variety of birds and other wildlife, plants and flowers, as well as an undeniable change in the British landscape. Happily, the removal of hedgerows has begun to slow down recently—experience has started to bring about a re-think.

Many of the plants which establish themselves in hedgerows do so with considerable ingenuity. Some, on fragile stalks, sway in circles in the wind until they find a support to twine themselves around. The wild Convolvulus and the Black Bryony twine in opposite ways; these positions cannot be changed, attempt to alter them and, in a few hours, they will either resume their former spiral course, or begin to wither and soon die. Some plants such as Bittersweet or Woody Nightshade can twine in both directions—with still others making a complete circle in a couple of hours or so.

Some weaker plants lean on other stronger ones while others, less well-mannered, such as the Bramble, not only leans on its neighbours, but hangs on to them with strong, sharp hooks. The Dog Rose uses this method, too, to hoist itself to the summit of the hedgerow, which is rather surprising for so delightful a blossomed and scented flower. It makes up for its rough tactics and unruly behaviour later in the year by providing us with hips for making into the syrup which is so rich in vitamin C. Maybe this is why the dog rose came to be selected as the symbol of pleasure and pain in the language of flowers.

Ivy, which denotes something true and lasting—not to be changed by the beating of the wintry winds—expresses ingenuity, too, in its growth. Its roots are not ordinary roots, for absorbing water and food, but designed to enable it to climb and cling to supports. While it grows on the ground, it does not produce flowers. When it uses tree trunks or hedges for support, and finds itself in the open air in the sunshine, it begins to prepare for blossoming. Without this, any blossoms or fruits would be unseen by the birds and insects. These roots of ivy always spring from that side of the stem which happens to be nearest to the support. The ivy never makes a mistake.

Many hedgerows contain Holly and, although both male and female holly trees have white, waxy, flowers, only the female tree bears the bright red berries. The blood-red berries and sharply spiked leaves are associated in legends with Christ's crucifixion and crown of thorns. According to another legend, the robin got its red breast after it tried to ease Christ's pain on the Cross and was splashed with a drop of his blood.

The stem of Honeysuckle, or Woodbine, in hedges often grows to a length of twenty feet or more as it twines its way through branches and taller plants. Its attractive yellowish-white and crimson-streaked trumpet-shaped flowers scent the air from May until September. It is particularly attractive to moths who pollinate it.

Anyone lucky enough to see the humming bird hawk moth in action will witness something remarkable. For, not only does it hover, vibrating its wings so fast that they become a blur, but it feeds at the same time, while poised in mid-air. It is one of the few insects with a tongue which, when uncoiled, is long enough to probe and reach the nectar at the bottom of the long, slender trumpets of the honeysuckle. Many who have watched this moth, which is about one and a half inches long, imagine they have seen a humming bird in Britain. The resemblance is remarkable, even down to the forked tail.

The moth is on the wing from June, arriving from southern Europe and often flying as much as 100 miles in a day. It not only visits the countryside, but gardens too. Like most living things, they have their good years and arrive in profusion, then there are the bad years. Sadly, they are seldom able to survive the winter. The caterpillars bred in a good year feed upon Ladies' Bedstraw. The fortunate moths which emerge migrate back to Europe—the others die in the winter.

The scent of honeysuckle is strongest at dusk when other long-tongued moths, such as lime hawk moths, are attracted to it.

Another occupant of hedgerows, Red Campion, is attractive but confusing to both man and beast. Each petal of its bright red or pink blossom is so deeply cut that there appear to be ten instead of five petals. Insects and other creatures will find the flowers open only in the daytime, and closed at night.

Red Campion grows beside hedges as well as in them and its hedgebank companion, Greater Stitchwort, which is a species of the pink family, has the five petals of its satiny flowers divided halfway to give the appearance of ten star-like petalled flowers. Its name arose from olden times when it was believed to cure the pain in the side, called 'stitch'.

Travellers through the ages had plenty of friends in the hedgerows. If they needed direction there was the Compass Plant, or Prickly Lettuce—a plant which grows in many countries, up to six feet tall on occasions, whose upper saw-edged leaves point north and south when exposed to sunlight. Although related to the garden lettuce, only young plants were used as a vegetable or in salads as older ones were said to be poisonous.

For travellers needing rest, there was Traveller's Joy. A hedgerow plant, also known as Wild Clematis, it often grows to a great height and provides good shade. Its other name of Old Man's Beard arose from its long, white and feathery seed-heads.

If they wanted to know the time there was Goat's Beard—a 'clock plant' whose strap-shaped yellow flowers open early in the morning and close by midday, hence its other popular country name of 'Jack-go-to-bed-at-noon'. Goat's beard is descriptive of the seed-heads with their feathery hairs.

Another 'clock' or 'sundial' flower found beside hedges (and in gardens) is the Scarlet Pimpernel whose brilliant flowers open around 8 o'clock in the morning and close about 3 o'clock in the afternoon. It was also used by country people and shepherds as a barometer or weather-glass—as the flowers always close before rain.

Honeysuckle and humming bird hawk moth, 'Lady's Bedstraw'
and caterpillar.

To accompany travellers on their journey there was Germander Speedwell to keep them safe and speed them on their way. The germander, with its vivid sky-blue flowers, belongs to eighteen species of speedwell grown in the British Isles—it is said that in Ireland this was actually sewn into the clothes of travellers to keep the wearer free from accidents.

Some hedgerow plants show great ingenuity in the spreading of their seeds. The heads of Burdock become sticky burrs which get entangled in fur or wool and are spread by animals. In Victorian times the burrs were used for what was considered a rude and rustic way of making love. It was a favourite amusement amongst country girls to pelt their rustic swains with the burrs—the coats to which they would not adhere must have been very threadbare.

A hedgebank plant used for a definite purpose, rather than just fun, is the Teasel. The heads, with their hooked spines, of the species 'Fuller's Teasel' have been used for years in the textile industry for 'fulling', or raising the nap on woollen goods and newly woven cloth. The prickly dome-shaped heads of purple flowers on their spined stems are both attractive and an excellent example of nature's engineering. When cut off in flower and dried they did the job so well, better than any man-made machine, that they were specially cultivated for the purpose—and still are, in some areas, to this day.

The seed-heads which appear in the autumn and continue into winter are much sought after by goldfinches, so many people cultivate teasel in their gardens. The dried heads are also used to good effect in flower arrangements.

Nature's own flower arrangements along the hedgerows provide perfectly designed shapes of height, colour, background and form. The Harebell (known in Scotland as the Bluebell) with its delicate bells of blue is one of the most beautiful of all wild flowers; one can almost imagine the chimes as the wind sways their blooms to and fro. When one looks closely at the fine tracery of white flowers on Cow Parsley it is easy to understand why it is likened to lace: it is known as 'Lady's Lace' in Somerset, and 'Honiton Lace' in Devon.

The Cowslip, yellowing the verges, its flowerheads hanging down on one side of the stem, have been likened to a bunch of keys, those of St Peter, in fact. Legend has it that when he was told that a duplicate key to heaven had been made, he let his keys drop, and cowslips rose from the ground where the keys fell.

The pink blossoms of Herb Robert also hang downwards—but only in rain, or at night. The stem is often of a red shade and towards autumn the fern-like leaves and whole plant tend to become red. This member of the geranium family, which is common in Britain's shady hedgebanks, also flourishes in Europe and the United States. In Britain, alone, it has well over one hundred English names, but the relevance of most is obscure, or has become lost.

Orchids always enhance any scene and the Early Purple Orchid is the earliest and most common of the fifty wild species growing in Britain. It is often seen as early as April; its distinctive spotted leaves and purple flowers continue to bloom for three months.

'*The bee went round to tell the flowers 'twas May*'.

One plant, with attractive pink and white pea-like blossoms, which continue to flower from June to September, is Common Rest Harrow. It was far from popular with farmers in the old days of oxen or horse-drawn ploughs or harrows. For, as its name implies, its long and tough roots made progress hard and slow. It used to be found at the edge of cornfields, where the harrow would come to rest. Modern tractors and farm implements make short work of the roots when encountered today, but it can still be seen flowering throughout Britain in grassy places, and on verges beside hedgerows.

Magnolia

THE MAGNOLIA, which is believed to be one of the oldest flowering plants in the world, seems to have been unknown in English gardens until about the time that St Paul's Cathedral was rebuilt after the Great Fire of London. Most species are native to North America and the Orient—the first to arrive appears to have come from Virginia, sent home by a missionary to Dr Compton, the Bishop of London, who grew it successfully in his Fulham Palace gardens, early in the 18th century.

The Chinese were amongst the earliest cultivators and honoured magnolia by placing it in the vicinity of their temples.

Originally, magnolias were known as laurel or tulip trees, before being renamed by Linnaeus and dedicated to the memory of Pierre Magnol, a former distinguished director of the French botanical garden at Montpellier. 'It is handsome both in foliage and flower and worthy of so fine a man', wrote Linnaeus. Pierre Magnol died in 1715, and the renaming of the plant to Magnolia didn't take place until 1753.

The original species sent to the Bishop of London from North America, known as the 'Swamp Bay', was given the botanical name, later, of 'Magnolia virginiana'. Many other American Magnolias followed, even more beautiful, with one which reached Europe in 1800 having leaves 3 ft long with flowers more than 1 ft across.

With so many different species growing in America it is not surprising that the Magnolia was adopted as the state flower of two of their States, those of Louisiana, and Mississippi.

When the plant hunters' attention was directed eastwards they obtained an even greater variety of evergreen and deciduous magnolias. One beautiful species 150 ft tall, with a mass of pink-crimson flowers, was found growing 10,000 ft up in the Bhutan Himalaya. Once introduced into Britain, it seldom grew more than 20 ft high, which made it more manageable in gardens but its culture required patience for it rarely flowered before it was twenty years old. There are still gardens in England, open to the public, where this magnolia can be seen.

Most of the magnolias grown in small gardens are Asiatic species with subtle, attractive colours, either in tree or shrub form. One of the most sought after is the one illustrated, 'magnolia × soulangiana', raised originally in France by crossing a white variety with a pink-crimson one, both of which came from China and were introduced to England from Japan.

Magnolias of various varieties still bring grace and charm to gardens throughout England as well as to many sites in London, where they can be

Magnolia with St Paul's in the background.

seen against the background of outstanding architecture. Within five days of the Great Fire of London being put out, Christopher Wren had carried out thorough research and drawn up a detailed plan for the new city centre. The plan had the sanction of Charles II, but administrative and other problems prevented it from being carried out. Wren, however, was not deterred and nine years later his genius and inspiration had led to the acceptance which enabled him to lay the foundation stone for St Paul's Cathedral. Thirty-five years later his son laid the last stone, with Christopher Wren still alive to see his great masterpiece completed. The year was 1710 and when Sir Christopher Wren died in 1723, aged 91 years, he was buried in the crypt of the cathedral, where there is the famous, but plain, monument with the inscription, written by his son: '*Si monumentum requiris, circumspice*'. (If you seek his monument, look around you.)

As we know, St Paul's Cathedral was Sir Christopher Wren's greatest monument but by no means his only one. Apart from many fine buildings he built throughout the country he reconstructed or designed more than fifty churches in London that had been destroyed during the Great Fire, amongst them, that of St James's in Piccadilly where, amid the paving stones of the courtyard, there is a magnificent magnolia tree which provides pleasure and inspiration to those fortunate enough to see it in bloom.

Foxglove

A fox may steal your hens, sir,
. . . If lawyer's hand is fee'd, sir
He steals your whole estate.

John Gay

IF THOSE LINES are considered unfair by some people (particularly lawyers), the Foxglove also has reason to complain in having been chosen as the symbol of insincerity. For, like the legal gentlemen, the plant is not only hardworking, it also gives much back of great service to mankind.

It may have seemed logical in olden times that the fox should be provided with a glove for, as a midnight marauder, a muffled hand might be of the first importance in the prosecution of his business. But, to our modern way of thinking, of what use is a glove, when what the fox really needs is four, fast, seven-league, silent boots?

The truth is, the foxglove has always been associated with fairies, goblins and the little people. And who amongst us has failed to be enthralled with the stories about the fairies, the land of make-believe they dwell in, and the wonderful things they do? Grimm's Fairy Tales, those of Hans Christian Andersen, Peter Pan and Midsummer Night's Dream still contine to enchant the young and not so young, alike.

Opinions differ as to the precise meaning of the familiar name of this noble plant which gives us so much pleasure in decking woodland glades, heaths and hedgerows and now, more and more, our gardens, with its purple, rose, crimson (and sometimes pure white) flowers.

The foxglove, or 'folk's glove' was worn by the fairies or little folk. Among its many local names are 'Fairy Gloves', 'Fairy Fingers', 'Fairy's Thimble' and 'Goblin's Thimble'—and there are many people who insist that it was the bad fairies that gave the plant to the fox.

In Norway, the plant is not the fox's glove, but the fox's bell, to provide him with music in the gloaming.

This much-loved plant is industrious—growing to a height of four, and sometimes six, feet with each unbranched stem bearing between twenty and eighty flowers on one side only, hanging head downwards. A landing stage is incorporated on the lower lip for the visiting bumble bees, on which the plant relies for fertilization. Nature's ingenuity has seen to it that the male, pollen-bearing organs of the flower are placed on the upper side of the petals so that the pollen is swept out by the hairy back of the bee who has to creep right in to reach the nectar at the base of the ovary. This is a good enough reason for the plant to be called 'Bee-Catchers' or 'Beehives' in some areas. As if this structure were not enough, a barrier of long, upright hairs is located at the mouth of the flower to prevent unwelcome insects from creeping inside to get at the nectar.

The foxglove is not only a joy to look at—it contains a substance from which the medicine *digitalis* is prepared, without which many of today's victims of the growing menace of heart disease would probably not be alive. The drug comes not only from the leaves, which are picked at the moment of flowering at the beginning of the second growing year, but also from the seeds.

The yellow-flowering species of foxglove, a native of Greece, and not grown wild in Britain, also contains *digitalis*.

But beware, and be 'foxy' when amidst foxgloves. Be content to admire them, for all parts of the plant are poisonous ... and there is nothing insincere about that warning!

Foxglove and bumble bee in woodland glade.

Roses

THE ROSE, which has been on the earth for millions of years, is the queen of flowers and came to be selected by the poets as the emblem of beauty for its form, delicacy of colour and exquisite perfume. Roses have no equal throughout the wide range of the whole floral world. Today, roses are the world's most popular cut flowers.

The long line of ancestry of the roses which we enjoy now probably goes back to the original wild Dog Roses. Discoveries in North America have revealed fossils of roses believed to be at least 35 million years old. Although there are species of roses native to almost every country in the Northern Hemisphere today, the dog rose still appears to be the one with the longest life. In the garden of the ancient abbey at Hildesheim, in Germany, there is a rose tree growing and flowering said to be over 1,000 years old. It is a form of dog rose and there are several legends as to how it came to be there. Some suggest that it was planted by Charlemagne, or by his son, but there is a more romantic story. The Emperor Ludwig, while out hunting wild boar one day in the surrounding forests, became separated from his attendants. As night approached he became lost and the only solution was to spend the night where he was. He settled down beneath a tree then, next morning, with the coming of the dawn, he was able to find his way back to his castle. Once there, however, he was dismayed to discover that he had lost a sacred relic. When it was found later in a wild rose tree near where he had spent the night, all attempts to extricate it failed. Ludwig gave up the struggle, turned his thoughts heavenwards, and promised to build a chapel there. Such vows were not made lightly and the chapel was built on the site where the 1,000 year old tree still grows today.

In another account, the fact that Ludwig would have been in danger from boars and other wild animals while sleeping in the forest was taken into consideration. In this version, after hanging his golden crucifix on a thorn bush, he prayed for protection. When his servants found him safe next morning, and woke him, Ludwig was amazed to see the transformation which had taken place overnight. His crucifix was no longer hanging on what was a thorn bush, but a rose tree. As in the other account, his amazement gave birth to the vow to build a chapel there. In time the chapel became an abbey, still with the rose growing high up its walls covering a vast area. Like St Paul's Cathedral, which still stands proud above London's skyline despite damage by air raids, the famous Hildesheim rose tree still grows and blooms against its ancient wall.

In every age, the rose has been more celebrated than any other flower. The Rose of Jericho, or Resurrection Flower, is said to have first bloomed at

Christ's birth, and to have closed its blooms at the Crucifixion, reopening at the resurrection. The five petals of the white rose were symbolic of the five wounds of Christ and red roses recalled the blood of the early martyrs. The rose motif can be seen today in the stone and wood carvings, as well as in the architecture of the 'rose windows' of many churches and cathedrals all over Europe: in France, for instance, at Amiens, Chartres, and Rheims, and in England at Lincoln and Westminster Cathedrals. At York Minster a Latin inscription in the chapter house reads: 'As the rose is the flower of flowers, this is the house of all houses.'

When 'rosary prayers' were introduced, the original rosaries, symbolic of Mary's rose garden, were made up of rose petals pressed tightly together, which gave off a pleasing aroma as count was kept of the number of prayers.

The association of roses with marriage ceremonies continued until comparatively recent times. Crowns of roses were placed on the heads of brides and rose petals were showered upon couples afterwards. Not everyone could be a summer bride, so artificial rose petals were made, to be replaced, eventually, by the easier to produce, but untidy, confetti.

For the most extravagant use of roses we have to go back into ancient history. Cleopatra had the floor covered with a thick carpet of fresh roses at a feast she gave to Mark Antony. At the banquets of Nero, and other Emperors, fortunes were spent on roses so that masses of blooms could float down continuously from holes in the ceiling onto their guests during banquets. The scent must have been overpowering and the enormous depth of flowers quite suffocating. With the passing of time, roses found their way into everything, even into mattresses filled with rose petals, hence the expression 'a bed of roses'. Token 'rose-rent' payments were made similar to those of the nominal peppercorn rents. Roses were made into wines, honey, conserves, medicines, as well as bath oil and perfumes.

The most expensive base of perfume comes from the fragrant oil, attar of roses. It is believed to have been discovered in India during the wedding of the Emperor, Jehan Ghir. As Jehan and his bride strolled along the banks of canals in gardens covered with rose petals, they enjoyed the perfection of this aroma of aromas, and noticing an oily substance on the water they arranged for it to be collected—thus obtaining the first attar. Ghazipur, on the Ganges, became noted for the roses from which this expensive perfume was made and gained the prize for the best attar at the Great Exhibition of 1851, at Hyde Park in London, although the attar from Kashmir was also superior to others. The main areas of rose production are near Grasse in the south of France, in Morocco, Turkey, and Bulgaria—the 'Valley of the Roses' at Sofia covers thousands of acres. The fact that such a vast quantity of flowers is required to make so little attar accounts for it being precious beyond price.

Fortunately, the leaves of the rose geranium yield a delightful perfume which so nearly resembles the real attar of roses that it can be added to it.

The rose is probably the first flower ever cultivated by man. Among the most famous rose gardens early in the last century was that created by Empress Josephine at the château she purchased at Malmaison, close to Paris, shortly after marrying Napoleon. It was a garden of taste and perfection, in which none but the best varieties of roses from all over Europe were allowed admission. After her marriage to Napoleon ended in divorce, it was to Malmaison that she retired to seek consolation amongst her roses. Her favourite flowers were immortalized in the rose portraits by Redouté.

The rose has not only been acclaimed by painters, but by poets such as Blake, Browning, Byron, Coleridge, Herrick, Keats, Shelley, Tennyson, and Wordsworth. (Shakespeare mentions the rose no less than seventy times.) This verse, by Robert Herrick (1591–1674), the English lyric poet, regarded by Swinburne as the greatest song writer, is but one example:

Gather ye rosebuds while ye may,
Old time is still a-flying:
And this same flower that smiles today
Tomorrow will be dying.

Modern hybrid roses.

The quarrel scene, in the garden of the Temple, London, between the dukes of York and Lancaster, rival claimants to the English throne, still makes a profound impression. The Duke of York defiantly plucks a white rose and Lancaster a red—their respective symbols in the Wars of the Roses which ensue. These are depicted by Shakespeare in *Henry VI*:

Richard Plantagenet:
Since you are tongue-tied, and so loath to speak,
In dumb significants proclaim your thoughts:
Let him that is a true-born gentleman,
And stands upon the honour of his birth,
If he suppose that I have pleaded truth,
From off this briar pluck a white rose with me.

Earl of Somerset:
Let him that is no coward, nor no flatterer,
But dare maintain the party of the truth,
Pluck a red rose from off this thorn with me.

Earl of Warwick:
I love no colours; and, without all colour
Of base insinuating flattery,
I pluck this white rose with Plantagenet.

Earl of Suffolk:
I pluck this red rose with young Somerset,
And say withal, I think he held the right.

Most fittingly (on what turned out to be one of the bloodiest civil wars which raged in England, from 1445 to 1485, during the reigns of Henry VI, Edward IV and Richard III) the scene closes with the prophecy of Warwick:

This brawl today,
Grown to this faction, in the Temple garden,
Shall send, between the red rose and the white,
A thousand souls to death and deadly night.

When the long and bitter wars finally came to an end, and the House of Tudor came into power, the peace was strengthened between the rival houses of York and Lancaster through the marriage of Henry VII (son of a Lancastrian) to the Plantagenet princess, Elizabeth of York. In fact the reconciliation was reinforced still further when the red and white roses were crossed and united into a single rose bearing both colours, produced by an English gardener named Miellez. This rose thereafter became the royal badge, and the emblem of England.

Various forms of roses have also become state flowers of America. The wild rose was adopted by Iowa, New York, and North Dakota, the American beauty rose being selected by the District of Columbia, and the Cherokee rose by Georgia.

A ceremony which takes place in London each year, known as the Ceremony of the Lilies and Roses, still honours the memory of Henry VI who was ousted from the throne during the beginning of the Wars of the Roses and imprisoned in the Tower of London, where he was finally murdered in the Wakefield Tower on 21 May 1471. Although he was only a few months old when he became king, and his subsequent reign was frequently marred by mistakes and misfortunes, he was interested in education and a patron of learning and founded Eton College in 1440, and King's College, Cambridge, a year later.

On 21 May each year, the anniversary of his death, representatives of both colleges walk in procession, with the beefeaters, to the Wakefield Tower where a short service is conducted by the chaplain—which includes a prayer written by Henry VI. Lilies, from Eton College, are placed on one side of the marble tablet where the king is believed to have died, and white roses from King's College, are placed on the other side.

Roses have featured in many other ways. They were worn in the bonnets of the Prince Charles' Highlanders as they marched south into England in 1745, and by the six English, Scottish, and Welsh regiments as they snatched them from the wild rose briars to put in their caps as they advanced across the heath towards the French positions at the Battle of Minden, in 1759, during the Seven Year's War.

Roses of every shape, form and colour have appeared on Valentine cards, introduced during the 18th century in order to replace the more expensive anonymous gifts which had previously been given. The hearts, flowers and verses were painted and composed by hand until printed cards appeared in the 19th century to save time and mental effort. They were an immediate success which lasted throughout Victorian times. When the rose was featured in the ballet *Le Spectre de la Rose* it had little need of a story—the dancing was enough. The red rose comes to life, dances, and finally says farewell as it soars out of the window. Nijinsky in this role made the greatest and most senational leaps of his matchless and inspired career.

The rose also achieved fame in another way when it was featured in the first ever 'flag day' to be held in Britain, on 26 June 1912, when the much beloved Queen Alexandra, widow of King Edward VII, started 'Alexandra Rose Day'. This event has become a British institution.

The story of this event begins in Denmark where there lived a priest who opened his home to crippled children, waifs and strays and never failed to offer food, help and comfort to those in need. Such a charitable heart was bound to attract an ever-growing 'family' and, with only a very modest income at his disposal, he soon found himself at his wit's end to know how to provide for them. Then he remembered his garden or, not so much his garden, but what it contained—the most beautiful roses which had given him so much pleasure and which, if he followed the thought through in his mind, could bring pleasure to so many others and solve his problem. So he cut them, sold them, and used the proceeds to help in feeding and clothing his 'family'.

The beautiful Princess Alexandra married Edward, Queen Victoria's eldest son. After thirty-eight years he succeeded to the throne. As King and Queen they both charmed the people and won much affection both in England and abroad. When the King died, in 1910, Alexandra devoted much of her time to charity and she remembered the story of the old priest.

As daughter of King Christian IX of Denmark, she had visited the priest at his village home just outside Copenhagen. Although this had been some years previously, she had never forgotten what he had done. His simple and original idea couldn't be bettered. She, too, would sell roses to help those in need. This, then, is how thousands of artificial roses, resembling the simple wild roses grown by the priest, came to be fashioned for sale by volunteers throughout the length and breadth of Britain. Alexandra Rose Day was established.

It was an immediate success, with the Queen herself crowning the proceedings, being driven in a carriage, bedecked with roses, and pulled by two horses through the streets of London to show appreciation to her hundreds of lady 'rose sellers' and many thousands more who bought and supported her cause.

Since then, the Alexandra Rose Days throughout the years, and other associated appeals, have been instrumental in distributing many millions of pounds — not to just one charity, but thousands. Covering the whole field of human need or misfortune: old people, orphans, cripples, the blind, the deaf, the mentally handicapped, the homeless; all these and many more.

As the queen of flowers is the emblem of beauty, it seems appropriate that all the patrons have been beautiful women: Queen Alexandra herself, her daughter Princess Victoria, Princess Marina, and her daughter Princess Alexandra (who became President in 1969).

The White Rose

THE WHITE ROSE has long been considered sacred to silence. Over whatever company it was suspended, no secrets were ever revealed — for it hung only above the festal board of sworn friendship. No matter how deep they might drink, or how long the wine-cup might circulate round the table, so long as the white rose hung over their heads, every secret was considered inviolable. No matter how trivial, or how important the trust, beneath that flower it was never betrayed, for around it was written the sentence, 'He who doth secrets reveal, beneath my roof shall never live.'

What faith and what confidence there must have been between man and man in olden times, when only the presence of a flower was needed to prevent the maligning whisper, to freeze up slander's hateful slime, and destroy that venom which, when once circulated, proves so fatal to human happiness.

Beyond the circle to which the expressive text was assigned, that wound about the rose, not a whisper wandered; only the pleasure was remembered, the painful word forgotten the instant it had gathered utterance — or, if

remembered at all, it was only as if having existed for a moment *sub rosa*, 'under the rose'.

The custom, which originated with the Romans, continued in England through the centuries to Victorian times when carvings of the rose in the plaster ceilings of dining rooms became popular, some of which can still be seen today. The carved rose symbol was also hung above the confessional in some European churches and cathedrals.

The Lily

THE WHITE LILY, which is the emblem of majesty and purity, is probably one of the oldest flowers in existence and believed to be a survivor from before the Ice Age. According to legend, when the infant Hercules was suckling at the goddess Juno's breast, as she slept some drops of milk fell on the heavens and became the Milky Way, with one drop falling to earth where it was transformed into the white lily.

The flower has been cultivated by man since time immemorial with its history, in some instances, dating back 5,000 years to the Assyrians. It is remembered most for its close connections with the legendary stories of the Virgin Mary. Artists for centuries have depicted the angel Gabriel coming to Mary, with a spray of lilies in his hand, to announce that she is to be the mother of the Christ-child.

The lily is also the sign of the Resurrection and, as such, the Easter flower. One story recalls that after the Virgin Mary died and three days later her tomb was visited, it was found to be empty except for lilies and roses.

Although the white lily was frequently placed as a token of purity in the hands of female saints, by artists in the Middle Ages, it did not become known as the 'Madonna Lily' until the late 19th century.

Jesus mentioned the flower during the Sermon on the Mount: 'Consider the lilies of the field, how they grow; they toil not, neither do they spin: And yet I say unto you, that even Solomon in all his glory was not arrayed like one of these.'

Pliny, during the first century A.D., gave details of how the bulbs of white lilies could be made to produce purple flowers, when soaked in red wine. Since when, we have learned that to gild a lily is to attempt, foolishly, to improve on perfection. Shakespeare, who mentions the lily in his writings on more than two dozen occasions, wrote:

> To gild refined gold, to paint the lily,
> To throw a perfume on the violet,
> To smooth the ice, or add another hue
> Unto the rainbow, or with taper-light
> To seek the beauteous eye of heaven to garnish,
> Is wasteful and ridiculous excess.

It is possible that the white Madonna lily was brought to England by the Romans for the therapeutic properties of its juice which was said to cure corns and soothe the sore feet of their legions after long marches. By Shakespearian times its flowers were fully appreciated for their beauty alone, with the plant being grown extensively in large gardens as well as those of country cottages.

In vivid contrast to the fair white Madonna lilies there are the many brightly coloured varieties of vivid crimson, scarlet, orange, golden tints and others. Amongst them the Turk's-cap lily, is said to have been introduced into Britain over 500 years ago from the mountains of Central Europe. Its attractive purple turban-shaped flowers, achieved by nature without resort to Pliny's recipe for steeping bulbs in red wine, are not only enjoyed in gardens but can sometimes be found growing wild in woodland areas.

Much of our enjoyment of flowers is due to the plant-collectors—William

Lilies.

Kerr, for instance, who introduced the Tiger Lily from Japan, via China, in 1804. Their journeys and expeditions often exposed them to great danger and hardships in which only determination could achieve any degree of success. The story of Ernest Wilson, one such plant-hunter, and his expedition to China in 1910, amongst others undertaken previously there, provides some indication.

While searching amidst difficult and mountainous country near the Tibetan border he suddenly came across a most beautiful lily—the Royal Lily. Hundreds of bulbs had been dug from the rock crevices when, suddenly, disaster struck in the form of a landslide which came crashing down and sent him tumbling hundreds of feet down the steep slope. A river lay below and, as his gyrating body attempted to struggle clear of the main course of falling debris, his leg was crushed and broken by a boulder. Bearers in the party could only fashion a rough splint when they arrived on the scene to help.

After a long and painful journey back to civilization, Wilson returned with bulbs of the Royal Lily triumphant, or so it seemed. The leg when examined, however, was found to be so badly set that amputation seemed to be the only answer. The only solution, that is, until he returned to America and a surgeon examined it, re-set the leg, and saved it for him.

Although left with a limp for the rest of his life, Ernest Wilson continued with his plant-hunting expeditions around the globe, before being appointed Assistant Director, and later Keeper, of the Arnold Arboretum, Boston. Then sadly, in 1930, after a lifetime of dangers encountered searching for plants in remote areas so that we, and millions of others could enjoy them, this eminent botanist, to whom we owe so much, was killed in a motor accident in Massachusetts.

The Shamrock

ALTHOUGH THE SHAMROCK with its three leaflets has been adopted as the national emblem of Ireland, and is said to have been used by St Patrick to illustrate the Trinity during the 5th century, there does not appear to have been any mention of it as an emblem until 300 years ago.

With its 3,500 miles of varied coastline, semi-tropical bays warmed by the Atlantic's Gulf Stream, rolling patchwork fields, lush greenery and some of the most unspoilt natural scenery in Europe, Ireland contains a wealth of exotic plants and wildflowers. Amongst them there are many small plants bearing trifoliate leaves all having been named shamrock, which has led to some confusion as to the identity of the true one.

Some people believe that the shamrock used by St Patrick was, in fact, the Wood Sorrel. To add to the confusion, when a survey was carried out in Ireland ninety years ago to decide which was the true shamrock worn on March 17, St Patrick's Day, claims were made for no less than a dozen plants with trifoliate leaves. A second survey carried out the following year failed to clarify things, and the debate continues to this day. Amongst the main contenders are White Clover, Red Clover, Hare's-foot Clover, Hop Trefoil, Lesser Yellow Trefoil, Black Medick and Wood Sorrel. None are in flower on St Patrick's Day but as the traditional symbol of Ireland is focused on the three leaflets which all these plants have, it seems that any will suffice.

Pinks and Carnations

THE CLOVE PINK, the ancestor of the Carnation, is believed to have been introduced into Britain by the Normans. This could have been intentional, alternatively pinks may have been imported accidentally on the Caen stone brought over for use in the castles and other buildings which they constructed. For years afterwards they were found growing on old castles and walls in Normandy, and subsequently in the same sort of habitats in Britain. Many of these cathedrals were originally built with Caen stone from Normandy, but erosion, harsh winters and, eventually, pollution in the more modern atmospheric conditions after the Industrial Revolution, led to its quick deterioration, with constant restoration necessary. Canterbury Cathedral is a notable example of the long and continuous process of restoration, but today's modern stonemasons use Lepine stone instead, which is also obtained from France. It looks very much like the original Caen stone which continued to be used for restoration work right into the 19th century, but it has a much longer life.

Considering the weight of the vast amount of stone needed to build castles, one wonders why the Normans didn't use stone native to Britain. Happily, it was easier to transport it across the Channel than to haul it overland from an English quarry—otherwise these members of the Dianthus family might not have reached Britain for many more centuries.

The flowers were still seen growing, in 1874, on the walls of Falaise Castle—William the Conqueror's birthplace—and like so many Norman castle ruins in England can still be seen to this day, as well as in Kent and Sussex which were the shortest routes across the Channel.

Dianthus comes from the Greek *dios* meaning divine, and *anthos*, a flower. In ancient times the Greeks used the flower in their garlands and coronets and, thus, from the early English word 'coronation', the name carnation was derived, as a cultivated variety of pink.

Pliny (A.D. 23–79), the Roman historian and naturalist, described how the clove-scented pink was discovered by the legions in Spain, where it was already used for flavouring wine. The custom was taken back to Rome and eventually found favour in England, where the petals became popular for flavouring ale as well as wine. As recounted by Chaucer in *The Canterbury Tales*, they were known as 'soppes-in-wine', and were used in this way during Shakespeare's time until the late 17th century; in the reign of Charles II they were especially popular.

The pink also found favour with the French in drinks, but of a different nature. When St Louis' Crusaders were afflicted by the plague near Tunis in the 13th century, the liquor they drank, mixed with pinks, had a medicinal quality which cured their fever. With gratitude, as well as foresight, they took the plant back to their country with them. Which is possibly one explanation of why the pink was called *tunica*, originally.

By the 17th century carnations were as popular in French gardens as they were in English ones. In 1793 they became linked with an historical event: the Chevalier de Rougeville dropped a carnation at the feet of Marie Antoinette imprisoned in the Temple during the French Revolution.

Carnations, with pinks growing outside.

Concealed within its calyx was a message containing details of a plan to rescue her. The guards pretended not to notice and did not intervene until she had pricked out her reply with a pin on a scrap of paper stating her understanding of the plan and appointed time of rescue. Then they moved in, intercepted the message, and put her under even closer guard—until taken to her execution.

The calyx of carnations continued to be used to conceal messages—despite failure on this occasion—but in a more romantic way of passing secret messages between lovers.

Carnations and pinks were the favourite flowers of both kings and commoners—from William the Conqueror, Edward III, and Charles II, to Edward VII and George V. Ordinary folk paid high prices, running into guineas, for nurserymens' plants at the height of the pink's craze.

One man, however, achieved lasting fame by raising his own variety of pink in a workhouse garden which he named 'Mrs Sinkins' after his wife. It happened in the 1870s when he was master of a workhouse at Slough and the event was considered such a notable achievement that the pink came to be incorporated in the coat of arms of the Borough of Slough.

Another man before him, early in the 18th century, a cloth manufacturer turned botanist, achieved fame when he discovered a certain wild pink growing on the 450 feet high cliffs of the Cheddar Gorge, in Somerset; it became known as the 'Cheddar Pink'. Few today remember the finder's name, Samuel Brewer, who later became head gardener to the Duke of Beaufort at Badminton. Though grown frequently in gardens since then, the Cheddar pink has become so rare in the wild that it is, now, a protected plant which makes it illegal to pick, uproot or harm this flower in any way.

Lily-of-the-Valley

IN SOME COUNTRY PLACES this humble but graceful plant is understood as pointing men's thoughts to a better world; it is called the 'ladder to heaven', a name evidently suggested by the arrangement of the bell-like flowers which always nod on one side of the main flower stalk. One of its local names 'Our Lady's Tears' arose from the appearance of the white flowers when seen at a distance and the legend of how Lilies of the Valley grew from the Virgin Mary's tears, shed at the Cross.

Despite its name it is not confined to valleys, and can still be found growing in woods. It is native not only to England, but to most of Europe where it grows frequently in the woods of France and Germany, as well as in

North America, and parts of Asia, China and Japan.

With its strong and pleasant perfume, and sound of spring in its very name, it is worn as a buttonhole on May Day in France, where it is known as 'Muguet de Mai'. Its high esteem has also led to it being selected as the national flower of Finland.

It grew in abundance on London's Hampstead Heath at the close of the 16th century and remained there, though gradually becoming less plentiful, until the early 19th century—and has been cultivated in gardens for well over 400 years.

Poppy

THE POPPY, which is one of the most ancient and revered of plants and tends to grow where ground has been disturbed, became the symbol of remembrance in two world wars because it grew in such abundance in the shell-torn fields of Flanders.

When it flowers and sheds the rough green calyx, it emerges with difficulty, like a delicate butterfly from a chrysalis—crumpled and flimsy and it, in the words of John Ruskin, 'remains visibly crushed and hurt to the end of its days'.

Sadly, too, the petals fall at the slightest touch for, as Robert Burns observed, 'Pleasures are like poppies spread—You seize the flow'r, its bloom is shed.'

The poppy was selected originally as the emblem of consolation, denoting sleep, rest, and repose. In Roman mythology, Morpheus, the god of dreams, fashioned crowns of poppies to give to those he wanted to send to sleep. The ancient Egyptians used the poppy in burial ceremonies as part of the gifts and utensils considered essential to ensure life after death. Well-preserved, dried poppies have been found in tombs dating from the time of the Pharaohs, over 3,000 years ago.

In Greek mythology the poppy is first said to have been raised by Demeter, the goddess of the harvest, who cultivated it amidst the golden wheat. The Romans worshipped this goddess, naming her Ceres—the origin of our word cereal.

According to the Greek myths, Demeter's lovely daughter Persephone was gathering flowers in a meadow when, suddenly, the earth opened and Hades appeared and carried her off to be his queen of the underworld. Heart-broken and in despair, Demeter, with torch in hand, sought her missing daughter far and wide throughout the world. For a year not a stalk of grain grew. When Demeter discovered where her daughter had been taken, she had forbidden the earth to bear fruit until she was returned.

Man would have died of hunger if Zeus had not persuaded Hades to let Persephone go. But as she had eaten a pomegranate with Hades in the underworld of the dead, she could not be allowed to stay away for ever. Consequently, Persephone had to spend three months of every year with Hades, then she was to be allowed to be with her mother on earth for the rest of the year. So it came about that during the spring, summer and autumn the earth blooms and bears fruit, while during the winter the crops sleep.

The story—since depicted in art and sculpture showing Demeter wearing a crown of wheat, with a lighted torch in one hand and a bunch of corn and poppies in the other—had a deeper meaning to many in the ancient world who saw in it the promise of a future life beyond death.

Poppies have brought scarlet glory to waysides and cornfields through the ages, and legends led to the belief that they were essential to the health of the corn. In more enlightened times their presence in cornfields was regarded as evidence of bad farming. It was no easy task to remove what farmers termed the 'Headache' for poppy seeds have been known to germinate after being buried for anything from fifty to a hundred years when the soil is disturbed.

In the Middle Ages the term 'poppy head' was introduced into ecclesiastical architecture to describe the groups of foliage and other ornaments placed on the tops and ends of church seats, benches and desks.

In early Victorian times country maidens still believed that they could test the affections of their lovers by the secret power which the poppy possessed. If one of the petals was placed upon the palm of the hand and when struck smartly made a loud report, their swains were true. If it burst in silence, it foretold that their lovers were false.

Although the common scarlet, or corn, poppy, which grows in countries all over the world, is to be found in diminishing quantities in Great Britain, it is the parent of the many varieties which still give such pleasure in our gardens. Amongst them Shirley Poppies named after the vicarage of Shirley in Surrey, around which there is a story which gives proof, if proof be needed, that a weed is only a flower growing in the wrong place to some, but a thing of joy to others.

It was in Shirley that the Rev. William Wilks came across some common wild field poppies growing in a waste corner of his garden adjoining the fields. Noticing that one solitary flower had a very narrow edge of white, he saved the seed. During the following years he obtained flowers which, all the while, got a larger white infusion to tone down the red until they arrived at quite a pale pink, with one plant pure white. He set himself the task of changing the central portions of the flower from black, to yellow or white. Eventually he succeeded in fixing a strain with petals which varied in colour from the brightest scarlet to pure white, with all shades of pink between, and all varieties of flaked and edged flowers too, but all having yellow or white stamens, anthers or pollen, and a white base. All this came from one single capsule of seed, raised from the common wild field poppy, which happened to find its way into a vicarage garden one hundred years ago.

Since the First World War the modest scarlet field poppy has achieved a prominence unequalled by any other wild flower in history. It changed from being the emblem of consolation to becoming the symbol of remembrance. The following verses captured the imagination of the British people in the dark days of trench warfare on the Western Front when so many young soldiers failed to return:

> In Flanders' fields the poppies blow
> Between the crosses, row on row,
> That mark our place: and in the sky
> The larks, still bravely singing, fly
> Scarce heard amid the guns below.

Poppies.

We are the dead. Short days ago
We lived, felt dawn, saw sunset glow,
Loved and were loved, and now we lie
    In Flanders' fields.

Take up our quarrel with the foe;
To you from failing hands we throw
The torch: be yours to hold it high.
If ye break faith with us who die
We shall not sleep, though poppies grow
    In Flanders' fields.

The verses were written by Colonel John McCrae, a Canadian, who had served as a gunner in the South African War, and at the outbreak of the First World War opted, once again, to join the fighting ranks. Having by then become a distinguished professor of medicine at McGill University, Montreal, the authorities decided that his abilities could best be used in that direction, so he was appointed as a Medical Officer and landed in France with the first Canadian Army contingent.

It was during a lull in the action at the second battle of Ypres in 1915, when in charge of a small first-aid post, that he wrote the verses in pencil on a page torn from his despatch book, then sent them anonymously to *Punch*, who published them under the title *In Flanders' Fields*.

With only six months to go before the Armistice, Colonel McCrae was brought as a stretcher case to one of the big hospitals on the French coast. On the third evening he was wheeled to the balcony of his room to look over the sea towards the cliffs of Dover. The verses were obviously in his mind, for he told the doctor who was in charge of his case: 'Tell them this . . . If ye break faith with us who die, we shall not sleep.' Shortly afterwards, that same night, Colonel McCrae died. He was buried in a cemetery on rising ground above Wimereux, within sight of the cliffs of Dover.

McCrae's poem by then was well known. The last verse, in particular, greatly impressed an American lady, Miss Moina Michael, who wrote a moving poem in reply:

THE VICTORY EMBLEM

Oh! You who sleep in Flanders' fields,
Sleep sweet—to rise anew;
We caught the torch you threw,
And holding high we kept
The faith with those who died.

We cherish too, the poppy red
That grows on fields where valor led,
It seems to signal to the skies
That blood of heroes never dies,
But lends a lustre to the red
Of the flower that blooms above the dead
In Flanders' fields.

And now the torch and poppy red
Wear in honour of our dead.
Fear not that ye have died for naught:
We've learned the lesson that ye taught
In Flanders' fields.

Just two days before the Armistice was signed some overseas War Secretaries of the Y.M.C.A. for whom she worked, and whose conference was being held at her house, presented her with a small gift of money. This she used to buy twenty-five red poppies, wearing one herself, which appeared to her to be the way to keep faith. Each secretary there also bought one from her. This brought about what can probably be claimed as the first group selling of poppies.

A French woman, Madame Guerin, took things a stage further when she visited various parts of the world and came up with the practical and useful idea that artificial poppies should be made and sold to help ex-service men and their dependants in need.

The poppies for Britain's first ever Poppy Day, held in 1921, were obtained from a French organization which used its profits to help children in the war-devastated areas.

The newly formed British Legion opened its own poppy factory in London in 1922 with its purpose—as it remains today—to give practical help in time of need to all men and women who have served in the forces, and to their widows and dependants.

Today, the Royal British Legion (the 'Royal' prefix was conferred in 1971) manufactures over 35 million poppies and 65,000 wreaths at Richmond in Surrey for its annual poppy appeal.

O you poor folk in cities,
A thousand, thousand pities!
Heaping the fairy gold that withers and dies;
One field in the June weather
Is worth all the gold ye gather,
One field in June weather—one Paradise.

Katherine Tynan

Meadows and Pastures

Nᴏᴛ sᴏ ᴍᴀɴʏ ʏᴇᴀʀs ᴀɢᴏ, it was possible to walk a short distance from any town and be in the countryside. While, less than fifty years ago, windmills could be seen on the skyline with many still in use grinding corn. They first appeared in England during the 12th century and at one time there were 10,000 of them. A gradual decline began at the beginning of the 19th century; the numbers had dwindled to around 300 in the 1930s. Today there are probably less than a couple of dozen still working, but the relics of many still

Meadow and pasture flowers with orange tip butterfly.

provide attractive landmarks—and one day we may even need them again.

Amidst the meadows and pastures of most country landscapes there are the red and white Clovers—more interesting than one might imagine. These provide a good fodder crop for cattle and sheep and account for the expression 'living in clover' which comes from their contentment in being offered such a delectable plant so rich in proteins and minerals. Clover also provides a large supply of nectar for bees, who visit the lower flowers first. After receiving their guest who pollinates them, the flowerhead bends downwards. As further visiting bees arrive they know that the nectar has been extracted and call on the flowerheads higher up.

The movement of the leaves is also interesting. As night approaches the two lower leaves move upwards towards each other until they are touching face to face, while the third leaf curls over the top to provide a protective roof over its companions. If you discover a clover with four leaves it is said to bring good luck, according to ancient belief.

The ancient Welsh bardic tales of the *Mabinogion* tell us of white clover plants which sprang up in the wake of Olwen wherever she walked—a girl with breasts whiter than the white swan, cheeks redder than the foxglove, and hair more yellow than the flowers of the broom . . . whose popular Welsh name signifies 'a white way'.

With such esteem for clover it comes as a suprise to find that such a useful, and even more beautiful flower as Meadowsweet should have become the emblem of 'uselessness'.

Thomas Miller, in his *Poetical Language of Flowers* written over a century and a quarter ago, dared to christen meadowsweet the 'Neglected Beauty'. For, as he said, 'a sweeter flower blows not in all the green meadows of pastoral England, and Neglected Beauty it shall ever represent to me, for it has been too long overlooked'. Miss Twamley, in her *Wild Flowers* says— and honour to her for saying it—'Its tall, red-tinted stems, handsome jagged leaves, and foam-like flowers, so rich in scent, and so very beautiful, well deserves the title so often bestowed upon it of "Queen of the Meadows".' The French and Italian names have both the same meaning—meadow queen. It fills the summer air with a scent like new-mown hay and hawthorn.'

Thomas Miller continues to press his argument further with his readers. 'Shall this sweet flower, so admirably advocated by a lady, any longer stand disgraced as the emblem of Uselessness, or will you not rather step forward and defend it as a Neglected Beauty, until some happier emblem is chosen? Just fancy one of your own sweet selves, for want of an advocate, so thrown back and insulted!'

Louisa Twamley (who later became Mrs Meredith) loved flowers and wrote about them, including a book of verses dedicated to Wordsworth, her contemporary, which he was pleased to accept. She also illustrated her own and other books. 'My models,' she wrote, 'always appeared to me too perfect in their beauty for me to dream of doing aught but attempt to copy, as faithfully as I can, their forms and colours.' (A most qualified and worthy advocate indeed.) Since then the 'Queen of the Meadows' has become much used and appreciated in England and all over Europe. It possesses one of the loveliest scents of the countryside—even the leaves, when pressed, release an almond-like fragrance. It has been used indoors to sweeten the air, and in drinks, such as claret and port, to make them even more enjoyable, as well as to give flavour to soups; the leaves and flowers make a fine herbal tea, and have many other uses of unrivalled medicinal value in which all parts, including the roots, have a use.

A plant to be found in Britain's grasslands and pastures, and many other parts of the world, which is always worth a closer look, is the Early Purple Orchid with its reddish-purple flowers and unusual narrow leaves, coloured with dark purple spots.

The Green Winged Orchid looks similar but is without markings on its leaves, and has a touch of green in the flowers.

Before the first coffee-houses were established in London in 1652, an extremely popular substitute for this drink was made from the dried and powdered roots of the early purple orchid—known as 'Saloop' or 'Salep' it was sold at London street-stalls. Once coffee arrived, the coffee houses became so popular as meeting places for social and political discussion that Charles II made an attempt to suppress them, describing them as 'seminaries of sedition'.

Although we still have coffee houses, a degree of restraint is needed so far as enjoyment of the early purple orchid and the green winged orchid are concerned—both are rare and should be admired, but not picked.

Another plant which was once widespread in Elizabethan and Stuart times, but which is becoming rare, and in danger of extinction from the ploughing up of old grassland and widespread drainage, is the Snake's Head Fritillary. Its general shape resembles a tulip, but with much narrower leaves, and a single drooping, nodding, bell-like flower. The buds tend to look like a snake's head—hence the name. But once fully open the red-purple and chequered, or mottled, pattern has been likened to that of a guinea fowl's plumage, also reflected in its Latin name. (Sometimes the flowers are white.) To see this strikingly shaped and patterned flower in a meadow is something the beholder will never forget. Many more people can enjoy them, however, if they wish, for fritillaries are commonly grown in gardens now, with new varieties of bulbs constantly being introduced.

Whenever the cuckoo can be heard the Cuckoo Flower will be in bloom.

Summer landscape—Field Poppy, Field Scabious, Ox-Eye Daises.

The plant, which grows throughout Britain, Europe and North America, gets its alternative name of 'Lady's Smock' through its resemblance, when seen at a distance, to female clothes laid out on the grass to bleach and dry. Seen close to, the flowers predominant colour varies from pale lilac to mauve. These flowers provide the perfect background to the orange-tip butterflies which are attracted to the flower. This name can be misleading though as it is only the forewings of the male which are orange tipped; those of the female are tipped with a blackish-grey.

A wild flower which gives yet more colour to the meadows is the Bugle with its blue blooms and dark purple leaves. There are many legends about the bugle and in some parts of Europe country folk still refrain from bringing it indoors for fear of the house being struck by lightning and destroyed by fire.

The tall Common Sorrel, with its dock-like flowers which become crimson when in fruit, adds still more variety to meadows and grasslands. Although the leaves have been added to salads, and the juice used in sauces, much as we use lemons today, the bitter taste does not agree with everyone. Sheep and horses avoid it as it can poison them.

Nature compensates, though, with the mallow family as sweets used to be made from the roots of the wild Marsh Mallow. They are made from pure gelatine and sugar today but the wild marsh mallow and the cultivated variety are still remarkable plants.

The Common Mallow is another interesting plant, with its alternative local names varying from 'Bread and Cheese', 'Fairy Cheeses' to 'Lady's Cheese', based on the flat nutlets of its rounded fruits shaped like the segments of a cheese and which children love to eat for their nutty flavour.

One of the most attractive of the wild mallows is the Musk Mallow, with its rose-pink flowers, which is also cultivated in gardens. It gets its name from the faint musk scent it emits when rubbed or taken indoors into a warm room.

Amongst the magic carpet of grasses which make up the meadows is the Barren Brome Grass which can be seen in Europe and North America. Cattle and horses will not eat it, but its decorative value in flower arrangements, or amongst other vases of grasses, is difficult to surpass. When dried grasses come into flower and are picked they should be hung upside down, or stood in vases without water.

Timothy Grass, with its tints of pink or white, which cattle do like, is named after Timothy Hanson who is said to have introduced it from England to America in the 18th century.

If a smell of new-mown hay is detected amidst uncut grass, the explanation will probably lie in the presence of Sweet Vernal Grass which

contains the oil 'coumarin' in the plumes of the spikelets, and gives the meadows their fragrance.

Quaking Grass is another grass which adds a touch of magic and decoration to meadows and the home with its purplish-brown and white egg-shaped spikelets vibrating in the slightest movement of air. 'Shivering' and 'trembling' are part of some of the descriptive local names, which also include 'doddering dillies' and 'wiggly wontins'.

It is impossible to think of meadows without Buttercups—so widely distributed throughout the world. Yet, the name itself for so universal and long-established a flower was first recorded in Britain only in 1777. Their presence in pastures was once believed to produce butter of a good colour. The flowers were even rubbed on the cow's udder to improve the milk. But, the truth is, animals avoid buttercups because they are poisonous, which is a good enough reason for humans not to suck or consume any part of them either. This need not stop the ancient practice, though, of children holding the flower under the chin which, if the skin turns yellow, shows that they like butter.

Water Lily

THE WHITE WATER LILY is the queen of the water and reigns sole sovereign over the lakes, ponds and streams. It was a species of water lily which the old Egyptians and ancient Indians worshipped—the most beautiful object that was held sacred in their superstitious creed—and one which we cannot look upon even now without feeling a delight mingled with reverence.

No flower looks more lovely than this 'Lady of the Lake', resting her crowned head on a green throne of velvet, while looking down into the depths of her own sky-reflecting realms and watching the dance of her attendant water-nymphs, keeping time to the rocking of the ripples and the dreamy swaying of the trailing water-stems.

William Cowper, the great 18th-century English poet—author of *John Gilpin*, many hymns, and such epigrams as 'God made the country, and man made the town' . . . and 'Variety's the very spice of life, that gives it all its flavour'—loved water lilies and spent many pleasant hours walking through the countryside, and gardening. Many of the cultivated varieties in our gardens today are descendants from this same wild, white water lily species that he so enjoyed.

Of passing interest, and connected only vaguely with the romance of life, there are records which tell us, shamelessly, that the rooting stems of the white water lily were used as a cure for baldness, and that passions were cooled in Elizabethan times by eating the seeds which were taken in broth.

The other wild water lily, which can still be seen on lakes, ponds and slow-moving waters, has smaller yellow flowers (supported on strong stems holding them above the water) which tend to smell of brandy. This, together with its green bottle-shaped seed-head, accounts for its alternative name of 'Brandy Bottle'.

One cannot think of water lilies without recalling the story about Joseph Paxton. A man of many talents, born poor and of humble origins, he was to have great influence on gardens and greenhouses during Queen Victoria's reign when he became head gardener at Chatsworth, owned by the Duke of Devonshire. The story starts many thousands of miles away on the River Amazon, in the early 1830s, when an explorer came across giant water lilies which had leaves six to seven feet in diameter, with upturned rims four to six inches high. The discovery excited the whole gardening world and, when seedlings were eventually raised successfully at Kew some years later, Joseph Paxton took delivery of one offered to the Duke of Devonshire, planting it in a large heated tank he had built specially for it in one of the conservatories at Chatsworth. Before long, the plant outgrew the tank and a new conservatory

Water lilies and dragonfly.

had to be built to house it. The plants at Kew had only managed to produce leaves and Joseph Paxton was determined to make this one flower.

He was particularly fascinated by the leaves and spent many hours studying them. Their upper surface was bright green, the underside a vivid crimson, but it was their structure that interested him. The hollow ribs radiating from the centre were between one and two inches thick, and branched into smaller linking struts to provide tremendous supporting strength and the necessary buoyancy.

As the plant spread more and more giant leaves it suddenly flowered, with many hundred petals of delicate shades ranging from rose and pink to pure white, varying from eight inches to double that distance across. The date was 2 November, 1849. *Victoria amazonica*—or *regia* as it was then called after the Queen—caused a sensation and Paxton lost no time in persuading his friends at Kew to come and see it—'The sight of which is worth a journey of a thousand miles'. When he announced the triumph to the Duke of Devonshire, who was then in Ireland, he wrote, 'no words can describe the grandeur and beauty of the plant'. Queen Victoria was fascinated, inviting Paxton to Windsor Castle to present her with one of the giant leaves and a flower.

Within a few days the Duke of Devonshire had rushed back from Ireland to Chatsworth to admire the flowers and witness a demonstration of the great supporting strength of the leaves. Paxton's seven-year-old daughter was placed on one of them and 'borne up for some time in perfect safety'.

Paxton was not only famous by now, he was also a director of several companies. When he was attending the meeting of a railway company in Derby, those present asked him for his valued opinion on a subject they had been discussing and which he appeared to be noting in detail on the large sheet of blotting paper in front of him. When he held up the sheet, instead of handwritten notes they were astonished to see a greatly enlarged drawing of the conservatory which he had built at Chatsworth to house the giant water lily. This, he told them, was to be his design for the iron and glass building to contain the Great Exhibition of 1851 in Hyde Park, London.

It was from this idea, based on nature's engineering and the extraordinary construction of the giant water lily's leaves which Paxton had studied, that the great Crystal Palace was built in the incredibly short time of seventeen weeks in Hyde Park, later to be re-erected on a permanent site at Sydenham where it was used continually until destroyed by fire in the 1930s.

Joseph Paxton's rise to international fame was almost as rapid as the speed at which he induced the giant water lily to grow and flower, and his crystal building to arise. From his humble beginnings he became Sir Joseph Paxton, Member of Parliament for Coventry, and director of many more companies. He died shortly after doing what he loved most—attending a flower show.

Lavender

It used to be said that no one had fully enjoyed the freshness of the countryside until they had slept in sheets that smelt of lavender. Izaak Walton, who portrayed the pleasures of country life so delightfully in *The Compleat Angler* was among those who knew the pleasure to be gained from sleeping between a pair of such sweetly scented sheets.

Lavender has always conjured up nostalgic images of English country houses, sunny cottage gardens ... and the famous perfume 'Old English Lavender'. This aromatic shrub, which is a native of southern Europe, was as much prized in ancient times as now for its refreshing perfume and cleansing properties. The Romans appreciated its many benefits two thousand years ago and used lavender to scent their baths. Its name being derived from the Latin *lavare*, to wash. Probably the Romans were responsible for introducing the plant into Britain.

Once cultivated, it was used for strewing between linen, as well as being put into sachets and placed in drawers, to impart an agreeable smell, and also to exclude moths! The mauve, or purple, flowers of this noble shrub not only looked lovely and smelt fragrant—the plant had other properties. It was used as an antiseptic on wounds and could cure many ailments. According to one European superstitution, it had the power of restoring speech.

Its appearance and perfume has given pleasure to countless millions through the ages. It was the favourite scent of Nell Gwyn and, like all lovers, Charles II gave her sachets of dried lavender tied up with ribbons. Commercial scent production in Britain had already begun early in that same 17th century and, although the extensive flower farms in the South of France were renowned for their fine perfumes, the 'Old English Lavender' became famous. The lavender grown on 300 acres near Mitcham, in Surrey, provided the essential oil of lavender of such high quality that it could command much higher prices than that distilled anywhere else. Later on, lavender came to be grown and distilled at Hitchin, in Hertfordshire, as well as in Norfolk and Lincolnshire.

Clematis, and Arbutus (The Strawberry Tree)

Fain would I climb, yet fear I to fall.

THIS LINE WAS written by Sir Walter Raleigh on a window-pane, under which Queen Elizabeth is reputed to have written:

If the heart fails thee, climb not at all.

Clematis does both these things as it is a vigorous climber to considerable heights, as well as a plant content to scramble over low-growing shrubs. It has been cultivated in gardens for hundreds of years with choice varieties owing their origins to the seedlings obtained by nurserymen from the wild clematis, or 'Traveller's Joy', so familiar in English hedgerows. The larger-flowered varieties were bred from species brought back by Robert Fortune during his plant-hunting expeditions in China.

Traveller's Joy, which is native to the British Isles, can climb up trees, by means of its tendrils, to 50 feet or more and live for over half a century. Its garlands of white flowers, with their sweet vanilla scent, which are without parallel for distinctiveness and beauty when woven around and through the hedgerows, provide further fascination with the coming of autumn, when the seed-heads change the scene (and give us the alternative name of 'Old Man's Beard') with masses of feathery, silky down hairs to provide a white foam which remains for months before being carried away on the wind.

Clematis, arbutus, and song thrushes.

Country folk in England, France, Germany and Holland used to smoke the plant by cutting lengths of the stem and lighting it when dry, which gave rise to alternative names such as 'Boy's Bacca', 'Gipsy's Bacca', and 'Poor Man's Friend'. While in Italy, the tender shoots were gathered for use as a pot-herb.

Today, there are over 150 species and hybrids of clematis embroidering the arbours, archways, pergolas and walls of gardens. Some varieties are used not as climbers, but as shrubby herbaceous plants.

Clematis can also provide an attractive decoration around disused wells, in gardens fortunate enough to have them. Although mains water is now taken for granted before its advent springs and wells were vital for human and animal existence. It is not surprising, therefore, that homage was paid to the spirits responsible for these miracles of underground water sources, since early times. With the coming of Christianity, however, pagan water-worship was forbidden, and most of the springs and wells were re-dedicated to the Blessed Virgin Mary, or to one or another of the Saints, and honoured annually with religious ceremonies.

One custom which was associated with these thanksgivings and blessings of the waters led to the highly-skilled art of well-dressing, in which large colourful pictures, ten feet or so high, were made with flowers and greenery to illustrate religious themes, and stories from the Bible. The pictures were built up on large wooden frames containing a flat bed of clay into which the outlines of the most elaborate and beautiful scenes were pricked out—ready for the insertion of all manner of flowers, petals, leaves and berries, tree-cones, bark and mosses and other natural materials. Well-dressing is still carried out in some areas of England, notably at Tissington, in Derbyshire, where a service of thanksgiving is held in the Parish Church of St Mary on Ascension Day, followed by the procession of villagers led by the clergy and choir to bless each of the five wells in the area, all of which are decorated with their own large floral pictures. Similar ceremonies are held in several other Derbyshire villages at Buxton, Barlow, Eyam, Stoney Middleton, Tideswell, Wirksworth and Youlgreave.

The well-dressings at Tissington, which usually contain the most elaborate designs, are perhaps the most famous, with the longest tradition. Some accounts suggest its origins date back over 600 years ago to when the Black Death caused hundreds of Derbyshire people to fall victim to the plague which was the scourge of the Country, while the villagers at Tissington itself escaped, supposedly due to the purity of its waters. Another theory leads to the belief that the custom started later during the drought of 1615 which lasted for six months, when the five wells of Tissington, unlike all others in England, continued to supply water without fail. The subsequent well-dressing was established by way of thanksgiving.

During the 17th century John Evelyn, the diarist and friend of Samuel Pepys, wrote one of his most famous works *Sylva*, published in 1664, which gave a detailed account of the craft of ironwork, describing the traditional methods used which remained unchanged in Britain until quite recently. The craft is a very ancient one which goes back at least 6,000 years, but during Evelyn's time charcoal was much in demand for forges and in the iron smelting industry where it gave twice the heat of an equivalent weight of wood.

Although charcoal is a valuable material in horticulture today, being used in potting composts, for instance, as well as in modern soil-less cultural methods, in those days the demand for charcoal did a disservice to the Arbutus, known as the 'Strawberry Tree', which though it was beautiful and stood for esteem and love in the language of flowers, was made much use of by the charcoal burners and thus had its numbers reduced. The charcoal burners were not ravagers of the forests and countryside, but men engaged in a craft requiring great skill. Just as all timber had its uses in the building of ships, homes and furniture, the Strawberry Tree helped to make good charcoal. Our regrets, looking back, should not be directed towards any criticism other than that it was a pity that such a lovely tree, already rare, with such delightful flowers and berries should have been made rarer. It appears to have made its way across Europe as far as Ireland where it still grows wild near the lakes of Killarney and in one or two other southern locations but it is not found in Britain, except in gardens, where its cultivation was first recorded in 1640. Arbutus also grows in Mexico and the United States, and has been chosen as the State Flower of Massachusetts.

One remarkable thing about the Strawberry Tree is that it sends forth clusters of little cream-coloured bell-shaped flowers between September and December, which look like lilies of the valley and also smell like them. These flowers then develop into berries which take a year to ripen, changing their colour from white to yellow and then from orange to red in the process. The final crimson berries have a rough surface, somewhat resembling strawberries in appearance. Because of the long time it takes for the fruits to reach maturity, sometimes 14 months, it is possible to see a Strawberry Tree bearing fruit of one season and blossom of another, or the fruit of two seasons at one and the same time.

The fruits themselves are used in some European countries for making wines and spirits, including France where jam is also made from them. Birds also eat the fruits which contain many seeds and thus assist in their dispersal. The hard red-brown wood is popular for making into walking-sticks, ornaments and decorative carvings.

Peony

THE PAEONY is named in honour of Paeon, a physician, who used its roots to cure Pluto of a wound inflicted by Hercules. The more familiar name is peony, a corruption that has the merit of a musical sound. It has been cultivated and a popular flower since the time of the ancient Greeks and been depicted in ceramics and art almost continuously since.

Considerable interest was caused when the plant was found growing on the remote island of Steep Holme, in the Severn Estuary, in the west of England, in 1803. As this particular species is a native of the Mediterranean, opinions differed as to how it got there. Some believed the plant must have been introduced during the Saxon invasion in the 6th century, but it seems more likely that they were brought in from Europe by the early Christians. The few places where the wild plants have since been discovered growing have almost always been close to the sites of former monasteries. Those found on Steep Holme were probably introduced when the monastery of St Michael was founded there by the Austin Friars in the 12th century.

The ecclesiastics and monks were the most educated people then, and in earlier times, and therefore had great influence. Arithmetic was considered so complex, for instance, at the time of the Saxons in England that it was said to be a study *too difficult for the mind of man*. The upper classes, even, were very uneducated during the Middle Ages, and as late as the reign of Edward VI (1547–1553) there were peers in Parliament unable to read.

One of the ways of teaching people, when few could read, as well as instructing them in the faith, was through the pictures seen in churches in the form of stained-glass windows. Flowers were featured in these picture windows, as well as in many of the wood and stone carvings, and ornamental mouldings. One of Britain's earliest historians, a monk called the Venerable Bede, wrote of craftsmen coming from France in A.D. 675 to glaze the windows of the church at Monkwearmouth, in the north of England. But it was not until the end of the 12th century, around the time of the monastery on Steep Holme, that the art of the stained-glass window established itself in England, in the decoration of churches and cathedrals.

The gardeners of the grand old tradition valued the cultivated varieties of the peony. In the time of John Parkinson (1567–1650)—author of the first illustrated English book devoted to ornamental plants and botanist to Charles I—the peony was to be found in almost every garden. As he observed, 'the double sort produces ripe seeds, which, being sown, bring forth some single and some double flowers.' Although still rare in its wild form, John Gerrard gave the opposite indication in his famous *Herbal* of

Peonies and passion flowers.

1597, when he said that he had found the peony growing wild near Gravesend. In the second edition published twenty-one years after his death, however, the editor wrote: 'I have been told that our author himself planted that Peony there, and afterwards seemed to find it there by accident; and I do believe it was so.'

Garden species of peony have been introduced to Britain from Europe, Siberia, China and Japan, as well as from north-west America in a variety of exotic forms and colours. The most beautiful of all, the tree peony, was brought from China over a century and a half ago.

One notable plant collector, Robert Fortune, searched hard for new varieties of the peony in China and, in particular, for blue peonies. The owner of a flower-shop offered to secure them from a village where he knew they grew—at considerable price, of course, for the location was over 100 miles distant. When he returned with the plants the specimens were poor and, more discouraging still, without a single blue peony amongst them. Being a man of his word, Fortune paid the high fee that had been asked, then learnt afterwards that the plants had been lifted by the flower-seller from someone's garden only a mile or so away.

Passion Flower

ONE OF THE MOST remarkably fashioned plants of all, and a long-established garden favourite, must surely be the Passion Flower, which was introduced into Britain from Brazil in 1699—in which all the instruments of Christ's Passion are to be found.

The crown above the petals represents the crown of thorns; the three styles, the nails; the five stamens Christ's wounds; the ovary represents the sponge soaked in vinegar; the ten sepals and petals of its blooms symbolize the ten faithful Apostles (with Peter who denied Jesus thrice, and Judas the betrayer, left out); and the outer corona represents the countless disciples.

Rosemary

SINCE ANCIENT GREEK, and Roman, times Rosemary was thought to improve the memory.

Shakespeare, who never allowed himself to gather an image from a flower or select it as an emblem without being sure it was appropriate, used rosemary as a symbol of remembrance. Ophelia, in her madness, gives rosemary to her brother, 'There's rosemary, that's for remembrance; pray, love, remember.' And who would wish to change the emblem of a flower which Shakespeare has immortalized?

For year after year, on Shakespeare's birthday—April 23, which is also St George's Day, a procession of flower-carriers have walked from the house where the poet was born at Stratford-on-Avon, through the town, to the Holy Trinity Church to place posies and blossoms on his grave.

Rosemary has played many parts: it has been used at feasts, festivals, and marriage ceremonies, and has even been used to stir the christening-cup. At funerals sprigs of rosemary were thrown into the grave, by way of promise to the departed that they would not be forgotten—a custom which continued in England until the 19th century.

There are many legends associated with rosemary: one of the most delightful tells us that when the Virgin Mary took flight into Egypt and her cloak swept over their original white flowers in passing, they changed colour immediately to reflect the blue colour of her cloak, and thereafter, the sky.

Begonia

IN THE LANGUAGE OF FLOWERS the Begonia represents 'dark thoughts'. Why this should be so is not easy to understand, unless it arises from the decision that has to be made whether to grow some varieties for their leaves, and others for their flowers. Either way, the choice will prove more than rewarding for the plant is noted for its profusion of flowers and wide range of brilliant colours, and delightful patterns of foliage.

The plant is native to most tropical countries, such as Asia, Africa and America and was named in honour of Michel Begon, a 17th-century French Governor of Canada and a patron of botany, who brought specimens of begonia back to Europe from the French Antilles in 1681, when on a tour of duty there.

Today begonias, in their wide variety, are popular everywhere—as designs on ceramics, as house plants, in gardens, and in the vast cultivation areas set aside for them such as in the fields of Belgium—equal in splendour to those of the Dutch tulip fields.

In Britain specialist nurseries are devoted entirely to begonias, aiming at perfection all the while. A winged capsule constitutes the fruit of the plant. The seeds which the capsules contain are minute and cost £1,500 per ounce, which is enough to produce two and a half to three million seedlings.

Nasturtium, Stock, Thrift

ANYONE WHO HAS seen sparks coming from the flowers of the Nasturtium probably thought they must have imagined it, but they are by no means alone in witnessing this extraordinary phenomenon. For in 1762 the daughter of the world-famous Swedish botanist, Linnaeus, described how at dusk on hot summer days she had observed the emission of these strange sparks. The spectacle was also observed, on separate occasions about that time, by the great German poet, novelist and philosopher, Goethe. The explanation is believed to have something to do with the high phosphoric acid content within the plant.

The main interest in the nasturtium, native of South America, said to have been introduced into England around 1596 by way of Spain and France, originally centred around the ability of its pungent and aromatic juices to ward off the dreaded disease of scurvy which was so common among sailors on long voyages. The plant is generously endowed with vitamin C, and by the 18th century the flowers and leaves were used extensively in salads, with the green seed-pods being pickled and used like capers, as they are to this day.

The species we cultivate in our gardens as climbers, for appearance, came to Britain from Peru towards the end of the 17th century. The creeping variety appeared much later in the 19th century. Today the Nasturtium provides us with a choice of attractive colours from yellow, orange, and gold to a deep coppery red.

During the days of sail, besides scurvy, sailors also had to contend with the ever-present fear of being shipwrecked. Navigational aids on board were primitive, with those ashore little better. Between the middle of the 18th and 19th centuries over one hundred ships foundered near St Catherines Point, at the southernmost tip of the Isle of Wight. In more recent times the young Winston Churchill was among others who happened to be at this spot when a ship sailed past as a storm blew up. Within minutes the ship had capsized, with a loss of 300 lives.

Apart from storms, one of the main reasons for countless shipwrecks was a lack of lighthouses, or their bad positioning which made them totally ineffective. Until disaster struck on this occasion, the original lighthouse was placed on a hill above the point where low cloud, fog and mists rendered it useless. The same mistake had been made at the dangerous, rocky, western approaches to the Isle of Wight at the Needles, where the light had been built 470 ft or so above sea level on the summit of the cliff where it was also frequently shrouded from view. Many years, and numerous shipwrecks later, new lighthouses were built lower down at both locations where they

Nasturtiums, stock, thrift.

could be seen by mariners. The present Needles light was established in 1859.

One thing the ancient mariners could not have failed to notice along the southern coasts of the Isle of Wight will have been the colourful masses of Stock which have grown along the limestone cliffs there for centuries, as they still do to this day. Stocks belong to a family rich in vitamins and other elements which were also useful in warding off scurvy. Time and cultivation have added, rather than diminished, the beauty of the stocks which flourished in the gardens of England's old baronial castles. They were known as Gillyflowers during Elizabethan times.

The Ten-Week Stock, so named because it comes into flower ten weeks after the seed has been sown, is a much-loved resident in gardens today. As, too, is the Night-Scented Stock which in the quiet of the evening fills the air with its exotic fragrance. This variety is in such harmony with the evening and night-time that it has been observed to open during an eclipse of the sun.

Another flower which thrives even when showered constantly with salt sea-spray, which grows on rocks, cliffs, salt-marshes, and anywhere where other plants can't get a living, is Thrift. According to one poet, writing over a century and a quarter ago, 'Thrift is a good old English name which ought never to be forgotten. From thriftiness begins comfort, independence, and everything which, with love, makes life happy; and should misfortune come, it meets with more sympathy than idleness and extravagance.'

In Elizabethan times thrift was known as 'Ladies' Cushion', while during the reign of George VI it achieved the distinction it deserved by being featured on the coins of threepenny bits.

Wherever it grows, by the sea, or on mountain tops (hence the Mountain Pink) the Sea Pink, Ladies' Cushion, or Thrift, is as popular as it ever was, and a particular favourite when placed in borders or rockeries.

John Keats and Henry Longfellow, the poets, both knew these flowers well and were inspired to stay and write some of their famous works on the Isle of Wight. Dickens too, wrote a large part of *Great Expectations* whilst living there. Alfred Lord Tennyson, poet laureate, and ardent lover of nature so enjoyed the seclusion and views from the downs above Freshwater that he climbed them almost daily from his lovely home 'Farringford' to sit for hours on end gazing out to sea, amidst air which he declared was worth sixpence a gulp.

A short walk west and Tennyson, too, would have seen the island's most famous landmark—the Needles—known for centuries to many thousands of visitors from other countries as they arrived by ship on England's shore.

Although the present lighthouse was erected during Tennyson's time neither he, nor we, can ever know the Needles as it used to be. For the narrow peninsula of chalky rocks obtained its name from a single needle-shaped pinnacle, 120 ft high, which collapsed and fell into the sea, without warning, on one perfectly calm day in 1764.

Seamen who still sail the seas on business and trade today, and yachtsmen who sail for pleasure, all have reason to be grateful to the Needles light, which can be seen from over 14 miles away, also to Marconi who, in 1897, successfully transmitted the first wireless message in the world, from this area, to a ship at sea.

In 1892, Alfred, Lord Tennyson had died, aged 83, and been accorded a public funeral in Westminster Abbey. But, in the year of Marconi's triumph, a cross of Cornish granite, almost 38 ft high, was erected on the High Down, with the inscription:

> In memory of Alfred Lord Tennyson this cross is raised, a beacon to sailors, by the people of Freshwater and other friends in England and America.

This cross is still visible now, high on the skyline, to the great man who wrote so many famous works, including *The Charge of the Light Brigade* and *In Memoriam*—perhaps his greatest poem—as well as many about nature and flowers, including this short sentiment which, like him, neither we nor any future generations of mankind will probably ever understand the answer:

> Flower in the crannied wall,
> I pluck you out of the crannies:
> I hold you here, root and all, in my hand,
> Little flower—but if I could understand
> What you are, root and all, and all in all . . .

Harebell

THE HAREBELL—the 'Bluebell of Scotland'—has been well chosen as the emblem of happy retirement. It is one of the most beautiful of wildflowers—adorning heath, hilly pastures and the sides of woods with its pure and delicate bells of blue. It has long been a favourite in Scotland, and England. Writings of over a century ago tell of the wild harebell 'which still gets as near into London as it can for the smoke, and may be found no farther off than Dulwich and Norwood, growing by the dusty roadside, under the shade of hedges, by dry ditches, and in spots where scarcely any other flowers are to be found. It may be seen nodding its beautiful blue head, alongside heather, when nearly all the blossoms of summer have faded.'

Heather

THE SONGS AND STORIES of Scotland are filled with praises of the 'bonnie blooming heather', which clothes the rugged Highlands with a soft vesture of purple. The Heath was well chosen as the emblem of solitude. It could scarcely be otherwise, adorning as it does the lonely waste, and waving over miles of desolate moorland where scarcely a tree breaks the low sky-line. It recalls many a wild landscape where there is little sign of human habitation: the bleak, broad mountain-side which throughout the long winter and the slow-coming spring looked barren until, towards the end of summer, when it was clothed everywhere with the rich carpet of crimson and purple heather. The scene looks, from the distance, as if a sunshine not of earth had come down and bathed the whole mountain in subdued and rosy light. The silence is only broken by the call of a bird, or a light-footed deer browsing in his heathery fastness, bounding off in a moment with all the fleetness of the wind when disturbed. These are places where the lizard peeps securely from its hole, and the wild cat glares from the deepest solitude.

Heather still evokes the solitude of the wilderness, and much else besides. The plant is an attraction to bees and a rich source of honey. In former times, it was used by Highlanders to build the walls of their 'shielings', or cabins, when mixed with mud and straw, and to thatch roofs. It was also used to provide a warm, comfortable bed for warriors and shepherds.

Common throughout Britain and Europe today heather, or ling, is believed to have been introduced to North America by the early settlers from the Scottish Highlands. White heather, however, is somewhat rare and in Scottish superstition it is regarded as a bringer of good luck.

The Scottish Thistle

THE SCOTTISH THISTLE stands for retaliation. When Alexander III was king of Scotland (1241–85), and Haakon, the king of Norway landed an army on the shores to conquer Scotland, it was thought a shabby thing to attack an enemy except in broad daylight. On one occasion, at Largs, the invaders resolved to avail themselves of stratagem, and to come upon the Scots by night. To prevent their tramp from being heard they marched barefooted. They thus advanced unobserved to within a short distance of the Scottish forces; one of the attackers unluckily set his foot on a superb prickly thistle, and he gave such a howl of pain that the Scots heard him.

They immediately ran to their arms and defeated the foe with great

Scottish thistle, heather, harebell.

slaughter. After this the thistle was, out of pure gratitude, made the emblem of the Scottish kingdom. It subsequently became the badge of the Most Ancient and Most Noble Order of the Thistle, founded in 1687 with the Motto: *Nemo me impune lacessit* (No one provokes me with impunity).

The Daisy

Of all the flowers in the mead,
Then love I most those flowers, white and red,
Such as men call daisies in our town.

Chaucer

ONE CAN IMAGINE Chaucer in fields powdered with daisies lying down, resting on his elbow, paying lowly reverence to this old English flower. For he tells us how he rose with the sun to watch the daisy open, and how he knelt beside it again in the evening to watch its starry rim close. It was his favourite flower and the only one which could lure the father of English poetry from his study and his books—over 600 years ago.

The daisy is the emblem of innocence, though Chaucer happily called it 'the eye of the day'. (The word daisy is a contraction of day's eye.) For his sake it ought to have been selected as the emblem of poetry, and throughout all time called 'Chaucer's flower'.

There is a country tradition that summer can really be said to have come when you can put your foot down on seven daisies at once. (For people with larger feet, the number is increased to nine.) Although wild daisies have been growing since earliest times and have been an inspiration to poets, to gardeners they are still a weed. The daisy, however, deserves to survive. It doesn't mind being trodden on; it puts down shoots from which fresh plants emerge, and ensures its survival further by putting down millions of tiny seeds in a comparatively small area of grassland. What is more, its bright yellow centre and ring of white petalled ray florets tipped with pink, are still regarded with pleasure and affection by mortals of all ages, young and old alike.

The larger Ox-Eye Daisy, which also grows in the wild, particularly in Europe and North America, is welcomed in gardens. Its alternative name of 'Moon Daisy' is well chosen; anyone who has seen its large white petals, with their golden centre, shining in the moonlight will agree that it does look like a full moon.

A popular pastime of maidens, continued into the present century, has been to recite 'he loves me, he loves me not' as they pull the petals off either form of these daisies until the final petal gives them their answer. While for those too young to think yet of love, there were always countless hours of fun to be had from making daisy chains on long summer days.

In France the daisy is called 'Marguerite' as it is associated with St Margaret, a patron of herbalists. The daisy family includes many choice garden varieties today. The name Daisy has been a popular choice for a girl's name for years. In fact, many an entertaining hour has been passed between friends discovering who can think of the greatest number of flowers adopted as Christian names for ladies. Rose has always been a favourite through the ages with variants, in different countries, of Rosa, Rosina, Rosabel, Rosalie, Rosamund, Rosette, Rhoda, and Rosemary—combining two Christian names in one. Other favourites used to spring to mind with ease—Iris, Ivy, Lily, Primrose, Hazel, Heather, Marigold, Myrtle, Olive or Olivia, Daphne, Violet, Veronica, Jasmine, Hyacinth—and Poppy.

In Scotland the daisy is called Bairnwort, which means the children's plant. In high summer, everywhere, children still gather the flowers to this day for their daisy chains.

Orchids.

Orchids

ORCHIDS, WHICH ARE among the most exotic of the world's flowers, belong to one of the largest families of flowering plants. They were first mentioned by Confucius, the Chinese philosopher, over 2,500 years ago with particular reference to their fragrance. The count of the number of different species within the family of Orchidaceae throughout the world today is still incomplete, though estimates put the figure at around 20,000 species. One of the reasons for the difficulty in counting them arises because they not only grow on the ground, but in trees, at sea level, and on mountains at altitudes up to 14,000 feet (over two and a half miles high).

Originally, as with most things of great ornamental value, the cultivation of orchids was limited to the wealthy. The demand in England and Europe sent the plant hunters all over the world to search for and send back more and more rare specimens. Though the rewards were high, competition was keen and their journeys frequently involved great personal risk. They faced shipwreck, the danger of falling down precipices, wading through swamps infested with mosquitoes, and all the hazards associated with tropical forests, as well as possible robbery, violence and death from bandits or cannibals. Despite this, the plant collectors sent vast quantities of specimens home, often many thousands at a time. These had to be transported over difficult country by both man and mule, and thence by sea for the long journey home.

The professionals—the botanists and naturalists—did their collecting and despatch job well, but those who received them at home let them, their industry, and themselves down. The orchid growers of both northern Europe and England did all the wrong things, for the right reasons. The plants from tropical areas needed warmth, they reasoned, so they put them in their 'stove houses' and applied lavish supplies of both heat, and water, and closed the doors to create the right atmosphere. They overlooked the need for fresh air and this, together with overheating, killed the plants.

It was soon discovered that different species needed different growing conditions, and when they mastered these and had piped hot-water systems fitted in their greenhouses, with boilers which gave them some degree of control, as well as improving the light and ventilation conditions, they were back in business.

The growers could see that each single seed capsule of their successfully grown orchids contained a mass of seeds. Today, with scientific measuring instruments, we know that many seed pods contain a million dust-like seeds which are so light that, in their natural state, they can be carried hundreds of miles by the wind. We also know that there are other species in which each single seed capsule can release two million seeds and one species which holds almost four million seeds. This vast number is necessary because each seed contains very little food reserve, most perish, and even those that survive to germinate are slow to grow.

Faced with such difficulty in reproducing new stock from seed, the plant-hunters were sent scurrying around the world once more. The searchers for new and rare specimens of plants carried out their work in great secrecy with each plant hunter putting as much effort into preventing others from finding out what he was up to or where he was, as in tracking down the specimens themselves.

As the flow of plants back to England increased throughout the 19th century, many nurseries started to specialize in orchids—amongst them the famous firm of Veitch & Sons of Chelsea, London. This family firm were fortunate enough to have a Scots gardener not only as a servant but as a friend of the founders who, with the aid of a surgeon who was also a keen botanist, defied orchid experts everywhere by proving that the hybridization of orchids was possible. When their successful cross produced its first flowers, in 1856, entirely new horizons were opened up. But new species were still sought after and the public demand for orchids, and the financial reward this would bring, led the captains and crews of ships travelling the world's oceans, as well as a whole host of other amateur plant collectors, to cash in on the boom.

By the end of the 19th century many hundreds of thousands of pounds changed hands over the imported plants in the auction rooms and at nurseries. The most valuable being the air plants which grew 100 feet or so up on the trunks and branches of trees in the tropical and subtropical regions.

Today the orchid is still much sought after everywhere but is now within the reach of everyone. Some are suitable, and greatly cherished as house plants for growing in living rooms. Countries everywhere from America to Australia, from the West to the Far East and in between, have provided the plants and helped to improve this most noble flower and make valuable contributions to various aspects of orchidology.

Britain, amongst the pioneers, is fortunate in having more than 50 species of orchids which grow wild. Some are only a few inches tall, others several feet high—but all are beautiful. Many are rare and endangered and so none, even though they may appear plentiful in any particular area, should be picked. Few wild seeds germinate and those that do take years to grow, and many more years after that before they reach the stage where flowers appear. Many take five to ten years to develop from seed to flower—even as long as fifteen years in some instances.

Laurel

THE LAUREL speaks of triumph or glory. In the Middle Ages this plant served to crown poets, artists and men of learning who had particularly distinguished themselves. From this practice we have derived our expression *poet laureate*.

From very early times it was the custom of the English kings to include poets and minstrels in their retinue. Instead of being crowned with laurel, however, they were granted pensions as a mark of royal favour. Such a pension, together with a pitcher of wine daily, was granted to Chaucer in the 14th century; Spenser, in the 16th century, was honoured in a similar manner. Ben Jonson was probably the first to hold a regular office as Court poet in 1616. John Dryden, who held the office from 1668 to 1689 being the first, so far as is known, to receive the official title of poet laureate. Amongst others, since, have been Southey, Wordsworth, Tennyson, and Bridges.

The olive-branch is a native of the Mediterranean, like the laurel, and the first plant mentioned in the Bible (Genesis: 8.11). Both olive-branch and dove are symbols of peace.

Chrysanthemum

ALTHOUGH THE CHRYSANTHEMUM has been cultivated in China for nearly 2,500 years, it did not reach England until about 200 years ago. Europe had received some plants a little earlier but without much success or enthusiasm. The first flowers were yellow with the original plant, known as 'Golden Flower', getting its name from 'chrysos', meaning gold, and 'anthos', flower. Today, with the wide variety of colours and flower forms available, it is one of the world's favourite flowers and almost as popular as the rose.

When the chrysanthemum was introduced from China into Japan at the end of the 4th century A.D., it was regarded as highly as in its original native land, with both countries continuing to devote much time and skill in improving on its cultivation, as well as portraying the flower for posterity in the pottery and paintings of their pictorial art. In time it became the personal emblem of the Mikado, with the Order of the Chrysanthemum (like Britain's Order of the Garter) being the highest honour possible to bestow. The chrysanthemum was held in such high esteem, in fact, that for some while only the emperor and the nobility were permitted to cultivate it.

It was also incorporated in the national flag which, contrary to popular belief still held to this day, does not contain the rising sun but a stylized chrysanthemum—a central disc surrounded by sixteen petals.

When a variety of chrysanthemum was introduced into Holland, in 1689, it did not survive and a century was to pass before the true Chinese chrysanthemum became established successfully in Europe. When, in 1789, M. Blanchard, a merchant of Marseilles, imported three plants, the white, purple, and violet, only the purple survived, and it was this variety brought from China to France and thence to the nursery of Mr Colville, at Chelsea, in 1796, which was the first to flower successfully in Britain.

A major breakthrough came thirty-six years later when seeds were raised successfully, followed by new arrivals of varieties from China, which renewed public enthusiasm, and led to the formation of the first Chrysanthemum Show held in the ancient city of Norwich. Other chrysanthemum societies were soon formed elsewhere in the country with that at Stoke Newington, which was then a village suburb of London, achieving fame all over the world after holding its first exhibition in 1846, and afterwards becoming the National Chrysanthemum Society. By then, the noble flower was truly established and within fifteen years the National Chrysanthemum Society exhibitions contained both Chinese and Japanese varieties.

Chrysanthemums.

Iris

ALTHOUGH THE YELLOW IRIS (also known as 'flag' because of the way it sways in the breeze like a banner) is the most common form of iris in the British Isles, the flower itself is steeped in history with its many different cultivated varieties cherished in countries all over the world.

In Greek mythology, the goddess Iris was the messenger of Juno, and goddess of the rainbow which served as a bridge to facilitate her frequent journeys between the 'Eye of Heaven' and earth. Her business seems to have been to cut matters short, and no doubt amongst the young deities of Olympus she often carried the important message of love.

A carved marble panel in Egypt, which has been studied by experts, gives visual evidence of the iris and a recorded history which goes back more than 4,000 years. But the historical event most usually remembered concerns the liking of the yellow water flag for lakes, streams, bends in rivers and shallow water, and an event which took place almost 1,500 years ago:

When Clovis, king of the Franks, was engaged in battle with a superior force of the Goths, and his army was being driven from the field, he thought of his queen, who had long been urging him to become a Christian as she was. Raising his eyes to heaven he promised to believe and be baptized if victory could be granted over his enemies. Facing the desperate situation, wondering how his army could cross the Rhine, his gaze was directed towards some yellow irises growing far out in the river. Knowing that these flowers grew on soil in shallow water he interpreted it as a sign from God and led his troops across with ease, and became victorious. On Christmas Day, that same year in A.D. 496, Clovis was baptized along with 3,000 of his followers. Previously, his emblem had displayed three toads. From then on they were replaced with irises.

The iris was adopted again later as the banner emblem of Louis VII when he led the Crusades in the 12th century, known then as the fleur-de-Louis ... to become the fleur-de-luce, or lys—both alternative versions of the name of Louis—or fleur-de-lis, which remained the royal emblem of France.

The other species of wild iris native to Britain is the Gladdon, or Gladwyn iris, with purple-violet and darkly veined flowers, which grows in damp woods, in hedgebanks, on downland and clifftops. It is also known as 'stinking iris', as it smells strange when its leaves are crushed. The blue iris is the state flower of Tennessee.

The iris is a truly international flower, cultivated in Japan, North Africa, Egypt, Spain, Italy, Greece, Germany, France, Holland, and in America— Mexico, California, and the states of Oregon and Washington in the USA.

Mandrake

SINCE MAN is subject to all manner of ailments and diseases, it is not unreasonable to assume that nature has provided him with cures to be found in the plants and flowers with which he co-exists.

There is, however, one plant with magical properties and healing powers worthy of mention, if only for the extraordinary qualities it possesses: its roots not only bear a resemblance to the shape of the human body, either man or woman, but also have the ability to shriek like humans when disturbed.

The exceptional powers of the Mandrake have been used as a cure for sterility in men, and to provide fertility in women, as told in the first book of the Bible (Genesis 30). Rachel, when she saw that she bore Jacob no children, asked for mandrakes. She then conceived and bore a son whom she called Joseph.

The mandrake, or 'womandrake', depending on how the root was shaped, gave life but it could also be deadly: it was said that when its long roots were pulled out of the ground the plant shrieked; anyone who heard the sounds was immediately struck dead. Shakespeare wrote of the mandrake's shrieks which 'living mortals hearing them run mad'. Similar legends are attributed to the White Bryony.

Besides its supposed influence on fertility when carried close to the body, the mandrake also contained valuable narcotic substances which were used in pain-killers and sleeping draughts.

Four Ages of Thought

CHILDHOOD

Sister, arise, the sun shines bright,
　　The bee is humming in the air,
The stream is singing in the light,
　　The May-buds never looked more fair;
Blue is the sky, no rain to-day:
　　Get up, it has been light for hours,
And we have not begun to play,
　　Nor have we gather'd any flowers.
Time, who looked on, each accent caught,
And said, 'He is too young for thought'.

YOUTH

To-night beside the garden-gate?
   Oh, what a while the night is coming!
I never saw the sun so late,
   Nor heard the bee at this time humming!
I thought the flowers an hour ago
   Had closed their bells and sunk to rest:
How slowly flies that hooded crow!
   How light it is along the west!
Said Time, 'He yet hath to be taught
That I oft move too quick for thought'.

MANHOOD

What thoughts would'st thou in me awaken!
   Not Love? for that brings only tears—
Nor Friendship? no, I was forsaken!
   Pleasure I have not known for years:
The future I would not foresee,
   I know too much from what is past,
No happiness is there for me,
   And troubles ever come too fast.
Said Time, 'No comfort have I brought,
The past to him's one painful thought.'

OLD AGE

Somehow the flowers seem different now,
   The Daisies dimmer than of old;
There 're fewer blossoms on the bough,
   The Hawthorn buds look grey and cold;
The Pansies wore another dye
   When I was young—when I was young
There's not that blue about the sky
   Which every way in those days hung.
There's nothing now looks as it 'ought'.
Said Time, 'The change is in thy thought.'

Thomas Miller

Wild balsam, hemp agrimony and flowering rush.

Cyclamen, Delphinium, Virginia Creeper

ALMOST 100 YEARS AGO a Cyclamen was presented at a meeting of the Floral Committee of the Royal Horticultural Society. The plant had at least 500 blossoms and was over seven years old, with a corm described as being 'nearly as large as a baby's head!'

Before anyone thought seriously about growing cyclamen in their gardens the interest originally centred on the corms which were a favourite of wild boar, and subsequently used as fodder for pigs—this accounts for the plant's alternative name of 'sowbread'. The corms were also much sought after in the apothecaries' shops, as a cure for all manner of complaints, including that of easing childbirth. Sixteenth-century writers warned of the perils for 'weomen with chylde' to ever walk over the root for fear of having a miscarriage. The opposite sex, on the other hand, went out of their way to seek out the underground tuberous roots for they were told, 'In case that a man's hair fall off, take this same wort, and put it into the nostrils.'

Cyclamen itself gets its name from the Greek word 'kyklos', meaning circular, which some accounts say referred to the shape of the individual petals, and others to the bulb-like root, while still others suggest that it was so named because the flower stalks of many species twist in a spiral after flowering. In any event, the leaves normally appear when the flowering has finished. Some of the smaller hardy varieties of cyclamen have been known to live for more than a century. Today, the soft colourings of pale pink or white petals, tinged with dark purple, are established favourites in gardens as well as indoors.

Delphiniums, known as Larkspur by our ancestors and referred to by them as being the 'Queen of the herbaceous border', are also tremendously popular today. Early interest in them however, like the cyclamen, was focused on the power of the seeds. During the mid-16th century, when powdered, they were 'strewed on children's hair to destroy vermin'. The plants, whose leaves are poisonous, kept insects away—as well as scorpions. The flowers were enough in themselves, when hung up indoors and looked at, to improve the eyesight.

Many of the old larger gardens and estates contained dovecots capable of housing over a thousand doves. Growing on their walls, as well as those of the house and garden was Virginia Creeper with leaves which turn scarlet and other fiery colours in the autumn. A creeping vine, sometimes called 'American Joy', with little self-clinging sucker-pads or discs which enable it to climb up flat surfaces without the need for tendrils or other support, it was brought back to England by John Tradescant when he visited Virginia in

1637. His father, also named John, who was gardener to King Charles I, died while he was away, and his son was appointed royal gardener to succeed him. Besides plants, the Tradescants brought home many other curious objects during their expeditions which formed the nucleus of a collection which came to be known as 'Tradescant's Ark'. An account of its contents published in 1656 included mention of such oddities as a stuffed dodo, 'two feathers of the phoenix tayle', and a lantern which had belonged to Guy Fawkes. These were housed in a museum the Tradescants had established as well as a physic garden at Lambeth, on the south side of the Thames. When the son died, the contents were bequeathed to his friend Elias Ashmole, an antiquarian, and they subsequently became a part of the celebrated Ashmolean Museum collection in Oxford.

The original species of Tradescantia, bearing their name, was brought by them to England from Virginia eight years before they introduced the Virginia Creeper. Tradescantia in their trailing form, with their great variety of colour and pattern of leaves, are widely used as house plants, while most of the garden varieties, bearing flowers, are derived from the plant obtained from Virginia, known by various other names such as 'Spiderwort', 'Trinity-Flower' and 'Moses in the Bulrushes'.

Elder

THE ELDER, which was so surrounded by superstition in the past that it is a wonder anyone ever went near it, has so many medicinal virtues that Boerhaave, a famous Dutch physician, is reported to have taken off his hat to all the elder trees he saw.

Every part of the plant, leaves, flowers, bark and roots have been used in herbal remedies since ancient times. Some of its 'magical' powers, however, were unpleasant and there were many things that country folk would not do with elder, such as use it as firewood, or make cradles for their babies from its wood. The slightest misuse led to dire consequences but, when treated with respect, the elder, it seems, was prepared to yield much.

Apart from being used to add flavour to ale, its flowers and fruit were stated over 250 years ago 'to greatly assist longevity' when made into wine. Today the distinctive flavour is still popular in home-made wines, jams and jellies.

In Britain, elder is mostly found growing as a shrub in hedgerows, and only occasionally as a small tree. Seed discovered during excavations of Stone Age sites suggest that it was used as a food. Its wood has been found to be the ideal material for making into wooden spoons and for carving chessmen. Many other uses were obtained from its stems and twigs which contain a pith. When this was removed, hollow tubes were formed to make musical instruments such as the sackbut and, in more recent times, penny whistles. The tubes when blown through were also used like bellows to kindle fires—and by children as pea-shooters. In the days of horse-drawn transport and farming it was common to place twigs of elder leaves in head-harnesses to keep flies away. Flies cannot tolerate the elder's strong musky smell.

In the autumn shiny black elderberries are particularly sought after by thrushes and starlings, and by waxwings, who fly over to Britain in winter when there is a shortage of food in their north European haunts. The waxwings' favourite food are rowan berries. When breeding is high and the season's rowan crop poor, they migrate to south Europe and Britain, appearing in flocks to descend on the countryside.

By the time they arrive, the blackbirds, starlings and thrushes, have usually stripped the rowan trees of their berries so the waxwings try other berry-bearing trees and bushes, including the elder. They can sometimes be seen feeding off berries in parks and gardens at close quarters as they are quite tame.

These invasions, or 'irruptions' as they are known, occur erratically—a

Hedgerow in autumn containing dog rose with hips, old man's beard, hawthorn berries, ivy in fruit, robin on holly, and sloes.

major one was recorded as far back as 300 years ago. But the most recent and most massive of all occurred in 1965–6 when more than 11,000 waxwings were recorded in two weeks at the peak of their arrival.

Sunflower, Michaelmas Daisy, Dahlia

'WHEN THE WORLD has enjoyed its laugh at the expense of the lovers of Sunflowers', wrote Shirley Hibberd in her *Familiar Garden Flowers* at the end of the last century, 'it may find a useful substitute for frothy excitement in "discovering" the maginificence of this very familiar flower. As seen in the average garden, its fine character is not often apparent, for it is usually badly grown, and the grave mistake is made of planting it in groups, whereas single plants should stand alone amidst green surroundings, and should be so liberally cultivated as to acquire gigantic proportions.'

Some three centuries earlier, grower after grower claimed to have produced the tallest sunflowers in cultivation. A height equal to that of a man was average, and certainly not worth boasting about. But while claims were made by botanists, writers and horticulturists of repute to have grown sunflowers in London gardens 14 feet tall with flowers which measured 16 inches across, there were those in Spain who claimed 24 feet, topped by some in Italy who had achieved a height of 40 feet.

Today, those who believe that 'small is beautiful' tend to go for the lower growing forms which are less overpowering and available in a wide range of colours.

The sunflower comes from South America. In Peru it was held in high esteem as the emblem of the Sun God of the Incas and was carved in the sculptures of their ancient temples, and woven in gold into the fabrics of their clothing. Every part of the plant had its uses. The stalks furnished them with fibre for their textiles, the leaves served as fodder, a yellow dye was obtained from its flowers, and food and oil from its seeds. Further uses have been found since—in salad and cooking oils, the making of margarine and manufacture of soap—and in artist's colours, which is appropriate seeing that it is impossible to look at, or mention, the sunflower without thinking of the Dutch painter Van Gogh, who captured the flower so vividly on more than a dozen canvases.

The flower not only resembles the sun, it was widely believed by poets and others to follow the sun, as suggested in these lines:

> As the sunflower turns to her god when he sets
> The same look which she turned when he rose.

Thomas Moore

Many people still believe this to be so, while the sceptics say they have seen gardens in full sun containing sunflowers facing in every conceivable direction at the same time. There is no doubt that many flowers do follow the sun and some, in fact, do it so faithfully that they twist themselves in such a knot that their heads fall off.

The sunflower, which came to Britain over 300 years ago, has been adopted in America as the state flower of Kansas.

Although Michaelmas Daisies (Asters) are native to many parts of the world, from Europe to the Far East, almost all in Britain have been introduced from North America. The plant got its name because it starts to bloom around September 29, the feast of St Michael.

The first plants to arrive in Britain were brought from Virginia in America in 1637 by John Tradescant, a Dutchman, son of John Tradescant the elder who was gardener to Charles I. In the language of flowers the Michaelmas Daisy has been chosen to represent 'afterthought' because it blows when the flowers of summer have faded—coming unaware, like a pleasant thought.

The Dahlia is another flower which brings colour to the autumn garden. It is a native of Mexico and was grown, with double flowers even, in gardens there over 400 years ago. It did not reach Europe until 1789, when seeds were sent by the superintendent of the Botanic Gardens of Mexico City to the Royal Gardens at Madrid. Within seven years seeds were sent by the wife of the British Ambassador, at Madrid, to the Royal Botanic Gardens at Kew. But, as with so many imported plants of those times, they died within a few years as their precise cultural requirements were not fully understood.

The plant was named after the Swedish botanist, Dahl and reintroduced into England in 1804. But, meanwhile, both Dr Dahl and the French Professor of the Natural History Museum in Paris looked upon the plant as a vegetable, rather than a garden flower. It was a vegetable, whose tubers they hoped would be enjoyed as much as those of the potato. The idea was worth pursuing for both Holland and Flanders had furnished England with vegetables before she cultivated them. Outside the Court the rest of the country scarcely knew the taste of them.

Such delights as asparagus, artichokes, cauliflowers, beans, peas and cabbages were not introduced until the reign of Charles II (1660–1685).

Dr Dahl and the French professor were to become disappointed men, however, for dahlia tubers could nowhere match the flavour of the potato and both England and the Continent rejected them.

Many of the French varieties reached Britain in the early 1800s and within a few years accounts of the time stated that the dahlia was 'the most fashionable flower in the country'.

Summer in Winter

AS EACH MOMENT of time passes it is gone for ever and can only become a memory. However, gardeners and country lovers, are fortunate in being able to stop time through the preservation of certain flowers; this enables them to capture the highlights of summer and autumn and continue to enjoy them through the winter. People have been preserving flowers and leaves for winter bouquets for centuries but, with all the knowledge, equipment and materials available today good flower arrangements are no longer conjuring tricks but rewarding works of art within the capabilities of everyone. As with everything else success, and the sense of achievement which accompanies it, comes from knowing what to do, and what not to do, through reading some of the many books available on the subject containing a wealth of helpful advice, and gaining inspiration from the work of others.

Dried flowers—Chinese lantern, globe thistle, Helichrysum bracteatum, hydrangea heads, sea holly, statice, teasel, Xeranthemum annum.

At one time or another many people have preserved beech leaves—as did Queen Alexandra; the coppery colour of the leaves is still enjoyed in many homes. It is not only leaves that are favoured but the foliage and fruits, seedheads and pods of all manner of plants which are used to make attractive additions to modern flower arrangements as well as stems of barley, oats, wheat and attractive grasses. Wild flowers are able to make their own contributions and preserve their natural colours just as well as the cultivated flowers from the garden. This is as long as all are harvested at exactly the right time and then dried in the approved manner for each particular type, or treated with drying agents such as household borax, sand, and silica-gel where recommended.

The orange and scarlet bell-like shape of the cases containing the fruits of the Chinese Lantern have been popular in winter arrangements for over 400 years, while the familiar and much-loved Statice, or Sea Lavender, have been developed to the stage where many pastel shades are available today. Teasel obtains its popularity from its dried flower heads which turn an attractive brown. The dried heads of Hydrangea provide maroon colouring; the blue or steely-blue flowers of the Globe Thistle dry well and keep their colour, like those of Xeranthemum with their white, pink and lavender colours, or Helichrysum with colours ranging from white and yellow to deep red.

The list of flowers which dry successfully, including those classed as everlasting is endless and the following are just a few:

Acanthus, Artemisia, Achillea (Yarrow), Bluebell, Bulrush, Burdock, Bells of Ireland, Chinese Lanterns, Carnations, Columbine, Catananche, Clarkia, Clematis, Delphinium, Fern, Foxglove, Globe Thistle, Grasses, Gypsophila, Honesty, Helichrysum, Helipterum, Heaths and Heathers, Hydrangea heads, Lilac, Lavender, Poppy, Pink, Statice, Sea Holly, Stonecrop, Thistle, Teasel, Xeranthemum.

These, and many others, skilfully arranged—whether in copper, brass, pewter, ceramic, glass or even miniature containers—bring colour and brightness to rooms and give endless pleasure throughout the long dark winter months.

Some of the flowers listed, as well as many others, including leaves and grasses, are also suitable for pressing, with the results being arranged in the form of collages, murals, framed pictures, personal cards, calendars, book marks, or in pendants, brooches and glass table-tops. Many people of all ages, unable either to draw or paint, discover hidden talents when they come to make up their flower arrangements in these various forms which are often works of art, and obtain pleasure in the new activity itself, as well as in the months and years of viewing afterwards.

Flowers have featured in music, poetry, art and architecture. The acanthus with its magnificent flowers and foliage is outstanding and is the emblem of the fine arts in the language of flowers. Its fame, which led to its incorporation in the classic architectural design on the capital of Corinthian columns arose when the Greek architect, Callimachus, saw it growing in unusual circumstances upon the grave of a young maiden.

A visitor had placed a basket, containing the young girl's toys and trinkets, on the grave and covered it with a tile. It was believed to have been put there by the girl's nurse, but what this lady did not know was that beneath the basket were the roots of an acanthus. When Callimachus came upon the scene it was spring and the plant had grown up through and around the basket, the dark green and deeply cut leaves having been bent back by the tile. The effect was so magnificent it inspired Callimachus to incorporate the design at the top of the columns of a temple he was building at that time at Corinth.

The flowers of acanthus, in keeping with the foliage, have a grace and beauty of shape and colour; the range of colour is from green and white to purple or red, according to the species.

Gorse, marigold, acacia, sweet pea.

Gorse

GORSE, FURZE, OR WHIN, is a pretty, though formidable plant, armed up to the very gold of the flowers, and piercing those who do not approach its beauty carefully.

The sight of gorse in flower on Putney Heath, London, so impressed the Swedish botanist Linnaeus during a visit to England in 1736, that he fell on his knees in rapture at the golden flowers to thank God for its loveliness.

Marigold

IN THE MIDDLE AGES the golden-yellow blossoms that grew in profusion throughout southern Europe were dedicated to the Virgin Mary and called 'Mary's gold' or marigold. The flower is often alluded to by the ancient poets, as bowing its head and mourning for the absence of the sun. A New Herbal in 1578 states: 'It hath pleasant, bright and shining yellow flowers, the which do close at the setting downe of the sunne, and do spread and open againe at the sunne rising.'

The marigold is *the* flower of the sun. It curls up its rays at sundown, and in the early morning the dewdrops nestle in the folded petals. Hence Shakespeare in *The Winter's Tale* wrote of 'the marigold that goes to bed wi' the sun, and with him rises weeping'.

The most moving reference to its symbol of grief was made by Charles I when prisoner in Carisbrooke Castle on the Isle of Wight, during the Civil War.

> The Marigold observes the sun
> More than my Subjects me have done . . .

Carisbrooke Castle was a major fortress, and is one of the finest moated Norman castle ruins in the south of England today. Escape was essential if the king was to have any chance of regaining the throne. Several attempts were made: in one of them the plan called for the king to escape by a rope from one of the windows. A horse was made ready to take him, under cover of darkness, to the coast where a ship would be waiting. But, when the time came, Charles was unable to squeeze his body through the window, so the escape had to be abandoned.

When Charles was executed, in 1649, the whole of civilized Europe was appalled. He met his fate with such dignity and composure that even one of his foes, the Puritan poet Andrew Marvell was inspired to write:

He nothing common did, or mean
Upon that memorable scene,
But bowed his stately head
Down as upon a bed.

As a man his record was beyond reproach—his faults were as a ruler, which prompted it to be said of him: 'No man so good was ever so bad a king.'

Despite their names, the French marigold did not come from France, nor the African marigold from Africa. Both are from Mexico and are assumed to have arrived in Europe together during the 16th century, although some believe it could have been long before then.

Acacia

THERE IS SOMETHING ABOUT the form of these beautiful flowers, as they droop and wave in the breeze, that conveys an idea of elegance and neatness, without being gaudy. They conjure up the image of a lady chastely, not garishly attired, and have been chosen as the symbol of elegance, friendship and secret love.

Sweet Pea

THE WILD FORM of Sweet Pea, which has a fragrant scent, was discovered in Sicily in 1697 by a monk, Father Franciscus Cupani, who sent some seeds, two years later, to a schoolmaster friend at Enfield, Middlesex. The flower was not generally appreciated, though, until more than a century later. Its subsequent colours and varieties became a great favourite of the Danish-born Princess Alexandra who became Queen of England, as the consort of Edward VII who came to the throne in 1901 after his mother Queen Victoria died.

There is something very beautiful in the mingled colours of the sweet pea, looking as if it were two or three different flowers shot out of the same calyx. It is like a little ship, with its rounded prow and arching keel, the hull of which is blue, overshadowed with sails of blended crimson and purple dyes. It resembles the nautilus, or looks like a butterfly alighting for a moment upon the slender stem, and . . . 'On the flower a folded pea-bloom swings'.

The Language of Flowers

THERE ARE MANY WAYS of looking at flowers—from a botanical or horticultural point of view, for instance, which is interesting ... or at their meaning and what they say, which is more interesting still. Almost all flowers are surrounded as if by a halo of meaning from the associations and memories of people in the past. This has given them a 'voice' and a 'language' and they have been potent symbols since earliest times. But there are some people who never understand their meaning, nor can they make out what is revealed by any of the other wonders of nature. Such are not desirable acquaintances. 'Keep far away,' says a wise man, 'from those who have no sympathy for flowers.'

The language of flowers came originally from the East, receiving a great deal of attention in Europe in the Middle Ages when it was of good service to lords and ladies who, in those times, knew as little how to write as how to read. It developed through the ages to become a universal language in which thoughts and feelings could be expressed, with additions being made, from time to time, by the poets, until a series of ideas was attached to every flower.

The simple nosegay could by these means be made to take the place of more formal epistles.

In France, where gentlemen have always placed great store in giving bouquets of flowers to their ladies, and still do so three or four times a week, at considerable cost, the language of flowers rose to a special prominence. It also had a great revival in England in early Victorian times when many books were written on the subject. Though most, with the exception of a few slight alterations and additions, were mere translations from French works.

Flowers were connected so vitally with romance it was important to understand their language and appreciate that each flower not only had its meaning but the way it was presented was significant. A flower in an upright position expressed a certain thought, but given with its head hanging downwards uttered just the contrary sentiment. It also made a difference if a flower was presented with or without its leaves, or without its thorns—if it happened to have any thorns. A rosebud, with all its thorns and leaves, meant: 'I fear, but I hope'; stripped of its thorns, 'There is everything to hope for'; stripped of its leaves, 'There is everything to fear.'

The expression of flowers could be varied by altering their position. The marigold, for example, stands for grief or pain. When placed on the head it signified sorrow of mind; above the heart, pangs of love; resting on the breast, mental weariness from lack of interest.

No flower has been more highly praised by poets in every country than the rose—the flower of love and beauty—so it is not unnatural that the 'Queen of Flowers' should have a leading role to play in the language of flowers. The sentiment expressed, however, depended on the colour. The white rose, employed as the symbol of silence, when presented to a loved one meant, 'I am worthy of you.' No doubt, a message of such conceit was often returned with the presentation of a dried full-blown rose declaring: 'Our love is over'. A yellow rose signified a 'decrease of love', or 'jealousy', while a white and red rose together formed a symbol of unity.

Several flowers together were used to express longer messages—or in the case of bouquets containing many flowers, as a form of correspondence exchanged secretly between lovers. A bouquet of old Saxon flowers containing broom, a Canterbury-bell, white water lily and rosemary said: 'Your humility, and constancy, and purity of heart, claim my affectionate remembrance.'

A bouquet containing gorse, marigold, acacia, sweet pea: 'Your anger causes me pain, your friendship and love are an everlasting pleasure.'

Of all the languages spoken in different countries, that of flowers exchanging hands is the only one which knows no barriers of frontiers or age—bringing joy to young lovers, and remembrances which occupy the quiet nooks of the heart as people grow old and savour memories of youth.

In many a drawer, attic, book or album, there must still be lurking the withered flowers of some past age—treasured, and if remembered, forming links which, when rediscovered, can connect and recall the past. Such flowers have been discovered in documents many hundreds of years old. A search today might well prove rewarding ... even if it only reveals a four-leaved clover pressed between some book's pages. This may be interpreted as a symbol of good luck, but in the language of flowers its simple but forthright message would have pleaded: 'Be mine'. If it was a red clover: 'Industry' ... or white: 'Think of me'.

THE BIRDS' LANGUAGE OF FLOWERS

Bower birds, which are native of Australia and New Guinea, use flowers to perfection in their courtship. There are several varieties and their bowers

vary considerably. One kind builds an elaborate tent-like structure of sticks, sometimes eight feet in height with little rooms, which is surrounded by a carefully tended garden of different coloured mosses and bright flower petals, fruits, feathers and shells. When these decorations become faded they are removed and replaced with fresh ones by the male, intent on impressing the female of his choice. Competition is keen; he not only has to be a good gardener, if he doesn't keep an eye on the garden his neighbours will steal its coloured contents for their bowers.

Another kind of bower bird builds a clever, but less elaborate, structure of two parallel walls made up of arched twigs and plant stems. Blue flowers and objects are placed near the entrance to entice the hen inside.

The bowers for courtship are always on the ground, and the nests are built in trees. A third kind of bower bird decorates the forecourt with specially selected leaves which he places on the ground with the pale side upwards. If a rival turns them over, while the owner is away, the cock immediately replaces them light-side up again upon his return.

Forget-Me-Not

THE LANGUAGE OF this flower lies in its name which arose, we are told, from the following incident. Two lovers were once loitering on the margin of a lake, when the maiden noticed some flowers growing on the surface of the water, near an island at some distance from the shore. She expressed a wish to obtain them and her knight, in the true spirit of ancient chivalry, at once plunged into the water, and swimming to the spot plucked the wished-for plant. His strength, however, failed and feeling that he could not regain the shore, although very near it, he threw the flowers on the bank; then casting a last affectionate look upon his lady-love, he cried, 'Forget me not!' and was covered by the waters.

This delightful, but tragic, story of the Forget-me-Not, which signifies 'true love', is said to have taken place just under two hundred years ago. In another version, of German origin, the waters in which the gallant knight drowned were not those of a lake but of the Danube, into which he fell and was swept away by the current after climbing down the bank to gather the flower for his sweetheart.

For centuries it had been the tradition that anyone who wore the flower would never be forgotten, nor forsaken by their lover. Henry of Lancaster, who later became Henry IV, adopted the flower as his emblem for the sentiment it expressed and also had it embroidered in silver-gilt and blue on the collar of his robe, together with letters of 'S', standing both for souvenir and sovereign. This collar fashion grew in popularity and came to be taken up by men and women sympathetic to the Lancastrian cause.

Many types of forget-me-not grow in England in a variety of habitat—by rivers, streams, ponds, on marshy ground, in woods and on mountains. The flower is widely distributed throughout Europe, parts of Asia, and the western side of North America. It has also been adopted as the state flower of Alaska.

One of the flower's English names was 'Mouse Ear', which is descriptive of the shape and woolliness of the leaves. The alternative name of 'Scorpion Grass' is used because of the resemblance of its stem to a scorpion's tail, which starts to uncurl as the flowers open. The plant was also said to be effective as a cure against the creature's venomous sting, although the fact that there were no scorpions in England seems to have been overlooked by the early English writers. Yet another variety, known as the changing forget-me-not, got its name through its ingenuity in producing yellow or white flowers when they first open which later change to bright blue.

Whether in the wild, or cultivated in gardens, the forget-me-not is a worthy flower with a plea for one thing . . . to be remembered!

Marsh Loosestrife, Marsh Marigold, Mints

TWO PLANTS WHICH LIKE damp conditions and are to be found growing in marshland or along the banks of streams or rivers, and ditches, tend to be confused as they both bear the same name of Loosestrife but belong to totally different families. The colours, however, enable a distinction to be made as one is purple, and the other yellow which belongs to the primrose family. Both flower between June and August, and are so attractive that they are welcomed in gardens. Cultivated varieties of Purple Loosestrife vary from pink and white to rich purple. While Yellow Loosestrife, which can also be white in its cultivated form, is known to have been grown in gardens since the 16th century, and quite possibly earlier.

Yellow Loosestrife used to be hung from the beams of cottages at one time for its ability to keep away flies. The smoke of the dried plant was also used for the same purpose, as well as 'to drive away serpents'. The Greeks and Romans believed that when branches of yellow loosestrife were hung around the necks of difficult oxen and horses harnessed to the plough that they became pacified and easier to handle. This probably arose from the plant's botanical name which translates as 'ending strife'. But its effect was more likely to have worked through its powers of keeping tiresome flies and other insects away. A yellow dye was also extracted from the flowers for many centuries and used as hair colour.

Another plant (which grew in England before the Ice Age) that brightens the spring and summer scene with its bright golden-yellow flowers in the same damp areas is the Marsh Marigold. It is a member of the buttercup family, and also known as Kingcup, Water Blobs, or May Blobs in some districts. At one time the young flower-buds were pickled and used as a substitute for capers but this is not recommended today as the plant is poisonous and is left by animals.

One plant growing in wet meadows and on the banks of streams and ditches is noticeable at first for its attractive pale lilac flowers. Its true identity is revealed through the strong smell of its grey-green leaves. It is the Horse Mint—one member of the vast Mint family and amongst those which grow wild throughout the country, and used as flavourings since ancient times. The family includes apple-scented Mint, Corn Mint, Peppermint, Pennyroyal, Spearmint, and the Water or Hairy Mint.

Pennyroyal appears to have been put to the greatest variety of uses through the ages to prevent giddiness, relieve headaches, cure coughs, and to freshen the drinking water of sailors on long voyages. It was also used to rid homes of fleas, and by cottagers to make tea, and flavour black puddings, hence its alternative names of Pudding-Grass or Pudding Herb.

The Globe Flower

A T THE TIME of William the Conqueror water mills were a familiar sight throughout Britain. Over 5,000 of them were recorded as being in use in his Domesday Book of 1086. Within sight of those mills many wild flowers grew, amongst them the Globe Flower, which has been described as the finest of all the buttercups that adorn moist meadows and riverside wastes.

The British species, which blooms from June to August, was once used in festivities in which country people gathered together to collect the flower for garlands to hang around the doors of their cottages, for decorating churches, and use in the well-dressing ceremonies to make up the intricate floral pictures of thanksgiving for the plentiful water supplies. The dried flowers were also used in Sweden to strew floors, because of their pleasant fragrance.

It was introduced in its wild form into country and London gardens in the 16th century, and its globe shape of attractive yellow flowers has remained unchanged since then.

In their wild form globe flowers are still common in Britain, particularly in the north. Although only a few water mills are still working today, the globe flower can be seen against the background of some ruined ones.

Valerian

EVERYONE KNOWS the story of the Pied Piper, the magician of German legend, who played his pipe to lure the rats of Hamelin into following him to the river where they drowned and who, because he was not paid, lured the children of the town away. The story was immortalized by Robert Browning in one of his many poems.

It is easy to understand why children should follow the music of a pipe-player but why the rats should have been influenced in the same way appears to be nothing short of a miracle. What we are not told, however, is that like many magicians the Pied Piper had part of his magic concealed in his pocket in the form of the plant we know as Common Valerian which has an irresistible attraction for rats . . . and cats, too. What happens when they both arrive on the scene of valerian growing wild, or in the garden, can only be left to the imagination. Possibly, they leave each other alone because both rats and cats become almost intoxicated with frenzied delight by the roots which, when dried, are used medicinally by humans as a powerful sedative to cure nervous attacks and nervous exhaustion.

Our ancestors called the wild valerian 'All-Heal', because of its tremendous curative powers. The name valerian is derived from the Latin *valere* which means 'to be well'. Chaucer used the old and alternative name of 'setwall' (or 'setewall'). The plant which is common in England, Europe and northern Asia, bears pale pink flowers.

Red Valerian which has red, and sometimes pink or white, flowers was introduced into English gardens from Europe during the 16th century. Although it is still grown for its attractive appearance in gardens today, it escaped from its early cultivation and earned the description in the language of flowers as having an 'accommodating disposition' through its ability to grow on old walls, ruins, rocky slopes and almost anywhere in the wild throughout the countryside.

Sea Bindweed, Sea Holly, Sea Pea, Samphire

> To see a World in a grain of sand,
> And a Heaven in a wild flower,
> Hold Infinity in the palm of your hand,
> And Eternity in an hour.
>
> *William Blake*

AROUND BRITAIN's 6,000 miles of coastline there are lovely wild flowers which show great tenacity in being there at all and an ability to survive the rugged conditions.

Sea Bindweed is but one example. Unlike its relative which twines a spiral course through the hedgerows, this maritime bindweed does not cling or climb, but uses its stems to creep below the shore, helping to stabilize the mobile sand dunes in the process. Its large funnel-shaped pinkish or pale purple flowers open wide during the day and close at night.

Sea Holly with its greyish-green colour and thistle-like heads of blue flowers, which make it a favourite in gardens and flower arrangements, also thrives on sand dunes in which its roots penetrate deeply. The roots were at one time boiled and used with sauce as a vegetable resembling parsnips, were also taken as an aphrodisiac, and candied as a sweetmeat known as 'eringoes'.

The Sea Pea, unlike its relative in the garden, uses its well adapted rootstock to establish itself on shingle beaches. The plant has provided food in the past. It came to the rescue of the inhabitants of Aldeburgh and Orford

in Suffolk, during a great crop famine in 1555, when it appeared on the coast there—the edible peas prevented the villagers from starving.

Samphire, which has adapted itself to grow on rocks and cliffs by the sea, has fleshy leaves which when young make an excellent pickle. Shakespeare writes of samphire being gathered halfway down the Cliffs of Dover, in *King Lear* and a chronicler almost fifty years after Shakespeare's time mentions the dangers of gathering Samphire from the cliffs of the Isle of Wight where those who adventured to do so 'buy their sauce with the price of their lives'.

Samphire is the herb of fisherman and derives its name *herbe de St Pierre* after the French patron saint.

Amaranth, Weigela

AMARANTH HAS BEEN grown in English gardens for centuries and was, at one time, a very popular cottage garden plant. It is an old flower, chosen by the ancients as the flower of immortality, and one of the flowers which was fabled to grow in the gardens of the gods. Milton mentions it—

Amongst those which blow in heaven, and make
The angels in their adoration cast down
Their crowns inwove with amaranth and gold:
Immortal amaranth, a flower which once
In Paradise, fast by the tree of life,
Began to bloom; but soon for man's offence
To heaven removed.

John Milton

Its trailing tassels of brilliant crimson flowers which have been likened to streams of blood led country women to call it 'Love Lies Bleeding'. There is also a pale green form, and both varieties make an interesting addition to gardens as well as to flower arrangements.

Weigela, which belongs to the same family as honeysuckle, is one of the larger shrubs which provides focal points of interest to gardens—its graceful arching branches bear a profusion of pink, rose, crimson, white or yellow flowers. The garden forms were raised from the rose-coloured weigela which was first seen by Robert Fortune, the plant collector, in the gardens of a mandarin on Chusan Island, in 1845, and sent back by him to England.

A Scattering of Seeds

WHEN ROSEBAY WILLOWHERB and Buddleia suddenly appeared amidst the devastation on London's bomb sites everyone was as inspired as a rallying speech from Churchill. No one could imagine how they got there. It made front-page news for it was a sign of hope—a light in a time of darkness.

Rosebay willowherb was a rare native species until it suddenly began to spread throughout Britain in the middle of the last century. The clue to its appearance on London's and other cities' bombed sites comes from its alternative name of 'fireweed', and its liking for burnt ground. Today, it can be found growing in areas where woods and heathland have been burnt, also along roadsides and, in particular, where ground has been disturbed, such as on railway embankments and building sites. It grows wild on vast areas in America. Its attractive colouring and appearance have also made it popular as a garden plant. Its ability to grow abundantly comes from its efficient method of seed dispersal. Each seed-pod has four flaps which open, when ripe, from the top—rather like peeling a banana—to release a mass of seeds, attached to silken hairs, which are so light that they billow like parachutes and float on the wind across the country, often for many miles.

Buddleia was discovered originally in Western China by a French missionary. It was introduced into Britain about thirty years after rosebay willowherb and, besides becoming popular as a garden shrub, it soon became naturalized in many areas by means of its tiny winged seeds. The honey-scented flowers, which vary in colour from lilac to purple, have a magnetic attraction for butterflies—peacocks, red admirals and tortoiseshells, in particular—hence its popular name of the butterfly-bush. The botanical name, *Buddleia davidii* honours the Rev. Adam Buddle (1660–1715), distinguished botanist and Essex vicar, and the French botanist, naturalist and missionary, Pierre David, who discovered and passed on so much knowledge of the fauna and flora of China.

Many plants have adapted most successfully to using wings or parachutes to enable them to travel considerable distances. Dandelions, thistles, traveller's joy or old man's beard, and goatsbeard are just some examples.

Dandelions and thistles have tufts of soft hairs which float on the merest breath of air. Old man's beard has long feathery plumes on its seeds which also float on the lightest breeze. The 'clock plant', 'goat's beard', or Jack-go-to-bed-at-noon, opens its parachutes only in fine weather. The feathery heads are much larger than those of the dandelion and if the air becomes damp while they are in flight, the silky parachute hairs close up automatically and fall to the ground where they may become lodged and thus germinate.

Once the flowers of coltsfoot have been fertilized they bend over like shepherd's crooks to prevent the rain from damaging the seeds. When these are ripe, the stalks straighten up and grow taller so that the feathered fruits are well positioned for the wind to carry them away and disperse them.

Distribution by the wind is by far the most effective form of dispersal and the seeds of orchids and begonias are so powder-like and small that gardeners hardly dare breathe when handling them. In the wild, the wind often carries them several hundred miles.

Some flowers just drop their seeds around them, but most need to spread their seeds where they will not be hidden from the sunlight by their leaves or those of neighbouring plants. Many use the ejection method, scattering their seeds violently. When balsam, 'Touch-me-not', the emblem of impatience, is touched it throws its ripe seeds out of the capsules with great force. The spread is even more effective when the seeds are shot on to water and then float away.

The pods of Cranesbill, whose fruit resembles the beak of a crane, also explode to eject their seeds. Geraniums shoot their seeds out, too. So do the pods of gorse, and the violet (the state flower of Illinois, New Jersey, Rhode Island and Wisconsin). Some seed-pods explode loudly. According to legend, broom was rebuked by the Virgin Mary for drawing attention to the infant Jesus when she was hiding him from Herod's soldiers.

Almost twenty years ago the seeds of an Artic species of lupin were discovered in ice of the Yukon and germinated successfully. Radiocarbon assessment showed them to be around 10,000 years old. The lupin is capable of throwing its seeds 11 yards (10 metres), but the poppy relies on its quantity of seed and the pepper-pot method. Each plant is said, by different authorities, to produce anything from around 20,000 to 50,000 seeds. Its fruit, which consists of a rounded capsule, has an almost flat top with a rim of holes through which the seeds can be scattered when the capsule is blown about by the wind. The seeds can lie dormant for at least fifty years, a hundred years according to some accounts, until the ground is disturbed and conditions are right.

Venus's Looking Glass, with its purple to lilac-coloured flowers, also has capsules with holes at the top through which its seeds escape. The plant gets its name from the shining seeds which look like miniature mirrors.

Many plants use hooks which catch on the fur and feathers of animals, and clothes of humans, to disperse their seeds. Agrimony, with its small golden-coloured flowers that cone up like a pile of stars, does this in hedgebanks and in the grass beside roadsides. Its appreciation of this assistance is acknowledged through having been selected as the symbol of gratitude in the language of flowers. It has long been valued by herb-gatherers in the country, and also has been used to make what many describe as excellent tea.

Other hooked flowers, such as burdock, spring to mind immediately, but the buttercup's use of hooks is probably less well known. The many fruits on each buttercup contain only a single seed and when these are ripe and fall to the ground their hooked ends ensure dispersal as they become attached to animals.

Birds are attracted to a variety of coloured fruits containing seeds. Sometimes the flesh of the fruit is sticky so that the seeds become attached to the outside of their beaks and, thus, they are transported some way before being wiped off—as with mistletoe. When other fruits are eaten, the seeds usually pass through the digestive organs unharmed, to be deposited in droppings, from which some thousands, from millions carried in this way, eventually germinate and mature.

The waters of streams and rivers are yet another carrier of land-based seeds, with the sea itself transporting them from one shore to another. While some water plants themselves enclose their seeds in a buoyant spongy capsule which floats some distance before becoming saturated, sinking, and settling on the bottom. The water lily uses this method, but as its seeds are embedded in fleshy pods an additional form of dispersal is brought about.

When the pods decay, they form a slimy mass which tends to smear the bills of waterfowl as they pick out the fruit inside to eat. The seeds on the outside of their bills are, thus, carried to other areas.

Some plants produce spores instead of seeds. Our ancestors believed that they had but to find the true fern seed, and carry it about with them, to become invisible. What would not a fond lover give for a packet of this fabulous seed, the ancient poets asked, so that he might at any hour steal unperceived into the presence of his mistress? However, the fern does not grow from seeds but from spores contained in little cases on the under-side of the leaves, which, when ripe, spring open, scattering the spores.

Each common field mushroom releases 16 million spores. When it comes to the spores of the edible cultivated mushrooms, experiments by mycologists and commercial mushroom growers show just how light these spores are. In carefully controlled still-air tests it has been shown that it takes 45 seconds for a single spore to fall one inch (2.54 cm) from the gills beneath a fully opened mushroom on to the surface of the bed below.

An opened mushroom placed gill side down on a flat white sheet of cardboard, and left, produces a fascinating radial pattern of the spores between each gill fanning out from the centre.

Hazel and Dogwood

During early Victorian times it was said of the Hazel, which stood for reconciliation in the language of flowers, that: 'The best way for young lovers to make up a quarrel was to walk into a wood, and seat themselves upon the flowers under the transparent leaves of the Hazel, for there they will soon become reconciled'. Another method suggested was to, 'join a nutting party in Autumn, for it is a very old saying "many nuts, many marriages", this old amusement, no doubt, having done much towards match-making.'

Hazel was cultivated by the ancient Greeks and Romans and had, for long, been considered magical and associated with all manner of powers. Apart from being able to afford protection against evil, and reconcile quarrelsome lovers, one of its most outstanding properties was the ability of a forked hazel twig to detect the presence of hidden underground water supplies. Water diviners were in considerable demand until comparatively recent times, when piped water supplies became available. Their art lay in their ability to hold the two twigs of the forked hazel apart, at precisely the right tension, so that when it passed over water it pointed downwards over the exact spot.

The detective power of the forked hazel twig also depended on the special powers of the person using it—not everyone possessed this gift. No satisfactory explanation has been given as to why it works for some people, and not others, or why the method works at all.

The wood of hazel was also used for making fencing and sheep hurdles, pegs and thatching spars, for the wattle in 'wattle and daub' buildings, as well as for walking sticks. Its brown nuts which ripen in the autumn, known as hazel or cob nuts, are so sought after as a pleasant and beneficial food that the coppices and hedgerows cannot supply enough. Although birds and squirrels like them they cannot really be blamed for the short supply as they form an important part of their diet, and they do assist considerably in helping to spread the hazel by dropping the nuts or, in the case of squirrels, forgetting where they put them. Some people grow them in their gardens, but the main source of the larger-sized cob nuts in the shops come from commercial orchards in England, Europe, Africa and parts of Asia.

A favourite pastime of country dwellers or visitors is to set the catkins, or lambs' tails, swinging when they are ripe and watch the clouds of fine yellow dust float away. This job is normally carried out by the wind, of course. Some of the dust is wasted but there is always a considerable quantity of pollen which falls on to the tips of open buds, each of which has a tuft of crimson thread-like flowers in the centre. When the dust reaches the heart of the bud the fertilization necessary for the production of nuts takes place.

Like hazel, Dogwood is both attractive and useful. Its fleshy fruits, which take the form of bluish-black berries, contain either one, or two hard seeds from which oil was extracted for lighting lamps, as well as in soap-making.

There are many species of Cornel or dogwood, which gets its botanical name from 'cornus', meaning a horn or horny, denoting the hardness of its wood which was used for making arrows, meat-skewers, mill-cogs, the handles of tools and in the fashioning of baskets, which was one of the most ancient of all the arts. Fragments of baskets have been discovered in archaeological excavations in many parts of the world, those in Egypt have been dated back 10,000 years and earlier in some instances.

The purplish-red stems and foliage of the variegated dogwood shrubs, particularly striking in the autumn and winter, have made them popular in gardens. The wild varieties are also common in Canada and many parts of the United States and the flowering dogwood has been selected as the State Flower of Virginia, and North Carolina.

Mistletoe

ALTHOUGH MISTLETOE has been used for centuries in Christmas decorations, the one place where it is not allowed is inside a church. This is probably because it was a sacred plant of pre-Christian religions, considered magical and associated widely with superstition. The only time it seems to have been pardoned for its pagan past was when it was granted admission to York Minster and placed on the high altar throughout the 'twelve days of Christmas' during the Middle Ages. There have only been one or two other occasions since then when mistletoe has been allowed among the evergreen decorations in churches at Christmas—and all these isolated incidents were in the North of England.

With the ban still in force in the more enlightened times in which we live, it seems to be a gross miscarriage of justice. For mistletoe brings nothing but joy. It is associated with peace and goodwill while, in the language of flowers, it stands for the truly Christian virtue of 'surmounting all difficulties'. So far as our homes are concerned, we know that Christmas can never be quite the same without it.

The English custom of kissing under the mistletoe is said to have arisen from an ancient Norse legend relating to Balder, the god of peace. In his life he had never known sadness and wherever he passed grief fled before the brightness of his presence. One night, however, his dreams were filled with premonitions of disaster. When his mother, Frigga, heard of this she was heartbroken and roamed the earth, pleading with all living things not to harm her son in any way, and all willingly agreed.

Balder continued to live a charmed life even when missiles and darts were thrown at him, all of them falling short harmlessly at his feet. His mother had done her work well but had forgotten one vital link in the protective chain— the odd-man-out and evil god Loki, whose nature was jealous and aimed to put an end to Balder's popularity and reign of love. With all the disguise and cunning he could muster, he learnt from Balder's mother that in her long and arduous journeys across the earth she had failed to find one plant—the mistletoe—and thus seek its promise of protection to her son.

When Loki went secretly to the oaks growing on the mountain side he, too, found it difficult to find the mistletoe. But when at last he did, he fashioned an arrow from the tough sprigs of the plant. Then, rather than involve himself, he chose one of Balder's greatest admirers, Hoder, who readily consented to throw the shaft believing that, like all other missiles, it could not harm Balder. But Hoder was blind, without any glimmer of sight, and as he threw the arrow at close range it struck and pierced the beloved Balder's heart.

The other grief-stricken gods restored Balder to life and entrusted mistletoe, thereafter, to his mother so that it would never again be able to inflict any harm, or touch the earth.

Although it was the evil Loki who should have been punished, the poor little mistletoe has been left to take the blame and that, according to the legend, is why it grows in trees instead of the earth. Ever since then, mistletoe was said to bring happiness and safety so long as it did not touch the ground, which is why, once mistletoe has been gathered, we always hang it up to denote friendship and hospitality; people who meet under it kiss in peace and love.

The Druids went to great lengths to ensure that mistletoe was never allowed to touch the ground. Normally, it grows on apple trees and is rarely found on the oak. To the Druids, mistletoe growing on oak denoted a sacred tree. When the mistletoe was cut by a priest a golden sickle was used, with the fulness of the white cloak worn being held out by others so that the mistletoe fell into it and not to the ground.

The mistletoe was divided among those present at the ceremony who wore them around their necks, and then hung the sprigs above their doorways afterwards to protect them from evil, and their dwellings from lightning and thunder. Sprigs of holly and mistletoe are still carried by the Druids at the annual midsummer ceremony and rites celebrated at Stonehenge today.

The ancient Druids also associated mistletoe with medicine and called the plant, which was used as the base of so many remedies, 'All Heal'.

The plant's ability to bring good fortune was used by farmers in Worcestershire until comparatively recently, when they used to feed it to the cow which was the first to calve in the New Year, in the belief that it would ensure success to the dairy and herd.

Mistletoe has been selected as the state flower of Oklahoma. The sprigs used in English Christmas decorations come mostly from the apple orchards of Herefordshire. In France, Normandy is a major commercial supplier.

Although the leaves and young stems of mistletoe are accepted as being of great service in medicines and the treatment of many ailments today, the berries are not used internally as they are poisonous. They are much sought after by birds, however, and in particular by the mistle thrush which is able to carry the seeds from the berries to a new host tree without harm to itself.

Flowers by any other Name

MOST PLANTS HAVE an alternative popular name and very often this bears such a striking resemblance to their appearance, action, or behaviour that the names are easy to understand. In other cases it requires some imagination to associate the name with the plant, while others have so many widely different names, sometimes running into dozens, and were named so long ago that no one can say for sure which is the correct explanation.

Associations with animals are frequent—the Bee Orchid and the Fly Orchid bear a remarkable resemblance to their namesakes, but it is not so clear which plants are supposed to be able to unshoe horses, serve as a substitute for soap, or which are called 'Cups and Saucers', 'Jack by the Hedge', 'Townhall Clock', or 'Gentlemen's Tormentors'?

Some of the names are anything but romantic and the flowers have every reason to complain—one of them does, but in doing so it has given pleasure and amusement to many people. For when the Sensitive Plant, a member of the Mimosa family, is touched during the day it immediately folds up its leaves, droops, and assumes a sleeping position. After a short while, if left undisturbed, it expands again and resumes its full beauty. It is believed to have adopted this habit in the wild as a defence against grazing animals, but still does so in its cultivated form in which it has long been enjoyed as a house plant. It came from Brazil originally and has attractive feathery green leaves; it bears pink flowers, which appear in clusters resembling small powder-puffs.

Another plant, known as the Obedient Plant, from North America, behaves differently. If the blooms are moved from one side to another on their spikes they remain in that position until moved again.

The popular name 'Snapdragon', for the Antirrhinum, comes from the action of the flower—when the sides are gently pressed the mouth opens wide, and when the pressure is released it snaps shut. The plant is a native of southern Europe, but no one knows for certain when it was introduced into Britain. It may have come with the Romans, or later with the Normans, but it has certainly been around for a long time and became thoroughly naturalized—it was growing on the cliffs of Dover at an early date. Subsequently it cast its beauty amidst the grey ruins of castles, abbeys, and old garden walls where it still competes with the Wallflower for the choicest crevices.

Amongst the oldest plants growing on the earth when it was covered with forests were the Horsetails. This plant is without flowers; its Latin names mean 'a horse' and 'a bristle' and it appears just like a horse's tail. In more recent times horsetail was used for cleaning pewter and saucepans.

Still on an equestrian theme, Horse-shoe Vetch obtained its name through the fruits of its pods which are arranged in the shape of a horseshoe. Coltsfoot distinguished itself through its leaves which are not only hoof-shaped but develop well after its bright yellow flowers, hence one of its other alternative names of 'Son Afore the Father'. A small fern known as Moonwort, or 'Unshoe the Horse', was said to have the power to cast the shoe of any horse careless enough to tread on it.

Some of the popular names referring to animals are fanciful, others are real. Anyone who has seen or grown the Monkey Flower cannot fail to have been impressed with the striking resemblance to a monkey's face, and by the fact that it is a very attractive flower. Or that their Shrimp Plant in the home really does have shrimp or prawn-shaped flower heads.

Whenever Cowslip is mentioned the emphasis tends to be put on 'slip', whereas it could well be 'lip' because the wrinkled texture of the leaves has been likened to a cow's lip. Cow Parsnip seems to have been misnamed, and the alternative of Hogweed seems more appropriate because the plant used to be fed to pigs. Sowbread, on the other hand, which is a form of Cyclamen, doesn't have to be fed to pigs as they root out and eat the tubers themselves. Although they are poisonous to humans, the pigs are not affected. Pigs are also able to eat acorns and are put out to roam the New Forest in Hampshire in the autumn, not only to supplement their diet but to prevent the free-ranging ponies from doing so as they can be killed by eating an excess of them.

Birds are featured extensively amongst the common names. The arrangement of the ripe fruits of Birdsfoot Trefoil resemble the foot or claws of a bird, while the leaves which consist of three leaflets account for 'Trefoil'. This plant has over 70 local names and the flower colours which range from yellow to orange, sometimes tinged with red, account for one of its more popular names 'Eggs and Bacon'.

The seed pods of Cranesbill closely resemble a crane's head and beak, with the Storksbill getting its name from its particularly long pointed seed-pod. The long scarlet tubes of a fuchsia-like flower from California account for the 'Hummingbird's Trumpet'. The deeply-cut red-coloured petals give the ragged appearance and name to the wild flower Ragged Robin.

For one of the longest of all local names we need look no further than Cuckoo Pint which, apart from being called 'Lords and Ladies', is also known as 'Kitty come down the lane jump up and kiss me'.

Before leaving animals, mention must be made of Goosegrass—much enjoyed by geese and goslings who, at one time it was said, kept themselves free of disease by eating it. The plant is also known by the name of

'Cleavers'—this is where the problem comes from for the stem, leaves and fruits have hooked hairs or bristles which catch in clothing and cleave to passers by. Though effective as a method of seed dispersal, it can be annoying, hence the alternative name of 'Gentlemen's Tormentors'.

Many plants get their names from their old-time medicinal use, such as Goutweed, used as a remedy for gout; Stitchwort as a cure for a stitch, or pain in the side. Eyebright is named for its supposed ability to cure eye troubles and improve poor eyesight, and Self-Heal, or All-Heal, is an excellent wound herb.

Amongst the many ancient plants having other uses was Soapwort with which a soapy lather was made from a small quantity of leaves and roots, boiled in water, to clean clothes, and wash wool before dyeing. The plant was, in fact, cultivated near the wool mills for this purpose. It was also used to clean the human body. It is still to be found growing in the wild with its cheerful pink, deep rose, or white flowers having encouraged its admission and cultivation in rock gardens and for trailing over garden walls. One of its local names is 'Bouncing Bett' which is used not only in parts of England but also in America.

Ground Ivy which has attractive clusters of blue flowers and hoof-shaped leaves which spread like ivy, but don't look like it, was once used to clear and improve the flavour of beer, hence its alternative name of 'Ale-Hoof'.

Garlic Mustard, which grows in hedges and gardens, was known as 'Jack-by-the-Hedge' and 'Sauce-Alone'. While the rosy-pink flowers with their creamy-white centres and apple-like smell of the Great Hairy Willowherb earned the plant the name of 'Codlins-and-Cream'.

The 'Townhall Clock', also called Moschatel, which flowers from April to May and is quite common in woods and thickets, is well worth looking at. It has five green flower heads with yellow anthers, of which four look outwards like the faces of a clock and the fifth points upwards to the sky.

The 'Cup and Saucer' plant, which comes from Central America and Mexico, starts off with green blooms which then become violet or dark purple within a few days. Another name for this climbing shrub, deriving from its shape, is 'Cathedral Bells'.

Many plants have been christened 'Mother of Thousands' through the abundance with which they produce leaves, blooms, or both, including those grown today as pot plants for the home.

One of the wild varieties, closely related to the Stinging Nettle, has green flowers and cushions of small green leaves which are produced at speed and in quantity to spread along banks and over walls. The plant is so busy, in fact, that this might account for one of its names 'Mind-Your-Own-Business'.

Flowers and the Sentiments they Represent

Acacia – Friendship
Acacia, Yellow – Secret Love
Acanthus – The fine arts, or artifice
Agrimony – Graditude; thankfulness
Almond, Flowering – Hope
Amaranth – Immortality
Amaranth, Globe – Unchangeable
Amaryllis – Timidity
Anemone, Field – Sickness
Anemone, Garden – Forsaken
Angelica – Inspiration
Apple Blossom – Preference
Aster, China – Variety
Auricula – Painting
Azalea – Temperance

Balm – Sympathy
Balm, Gentle – Pleasantry
Balm of Gilead – Cure; relief
Balsam – Impatience
Bee Orchis – Industry
Bee Ophrys – Error
Begonia – Dark Thoughts
Betony – Surprise
Bilberry – Treachery
Birdsfoot Trefoil – Revenge
Blackthorn – Difficulty
Bluebell – Constancy
Bluebottle (Centaury) – Delicacy
Borage – Bluntness
Bramble – Lowliness; envy
Broom – Humility; neatness
Bugloss – Falsehood
Bulrush – Docility
Burdock – Rudeness
Buttercup – Ingratitude
Butterfly Orchis – Gaiety

Calycanthus – Benevolence

Camellia Japonica – Excellence
Candytuft – Indifference
Canterbury Bell –
  Acknowledgement; gratitude;
  constancy
Cardamine (Cuckoo Flower) –
  Paternal error
Cardinal Flower – Distinction
Carnation, Red – Alas! for my poor
  heart
Carnation, Striped – Refusal
Carnation, Yellow – Disdain
Catchfly – Deceit
Celandine – Joys to come
Cherry Tree – Education
Cherry Tree, White – Deception
China Aster – Variety
China Aster, Double – I partake your
  sentiments
China Aster, Single – I will think of it
Chrysanthemum, China –
  Cheerfulness under misfortune
Chrysanthemum, Red – I love
Chrysanthemum, White – Truth
Chrysanthemum, Yellow – Slighted
  Love
Cinquefoil – Maternal affection
Clematis – Mental beauty
Clematis, Evergreen – Poverty
Clover, Four-Leaved – Be mine
Clover, Red – Industry
Clover, White – Think of me
Coltsfoot – Justice shall be done
Columbine – Folly; frivolity
Columbine, Purple – Resolution
Columbine, Red – Anxious and
  trembling
Convolvulus – Repose
Corn – Riches

Cowslip – Pensiveness
Cowslip, American – You are my divinity
Crab Blossom – Ill-nature
Cranberry – Cure for heartache
Cranesbill – Envy
Crocus – Abuse not
Crocus, Spring – Youthful gladness
Crown Imperial – Majesty; power
Cyclamen – Diffidence

Daffodil – Regard
Dahlia – Elegance and dignity
Daisy – Innocence
Daisy, Garden – I share your sentiments
Daisy, Michaelmas – Afterthought
Daisy, Ox-Eye – A Token
Dandelion – Foresight
Daphne Odora – Painting the lily
Dew Plant – A serenade
Dittany of Crete – Birth
Dittany, White – Passion
Dock – Patience
Dogwood – Durability

Eglantine (or Sweet Briar) – Poetry
Elder – Zealousness; compassion

Fennel – Strength
Fern – Sincerity
Flax – I feel your kindness; domestic industry
Fleur-de-Lys – Flame
Flowering reed – Confidence in heaven
Flower-of-an-Hour – Delicate beauty
Fly Orchis – Error
Forget-me-not – Forget me not
Foxglove – Insincerity
Fuchsia – Taste

Geranium, Dark – Melancholy
Geranium, Nutmeg – An expected meeting
Geranium, Oak-Leaved – Lady, deign to smile
Geranium, Pencil-Leaved – Ingenuity
Geranium, Rose or Pink – Preference
Geranium, Scarlet – Comforting
Geranium, Silver-Leaved – Recall
Geranium, Wild – Steadfast piety
Gladioli – Bonds of affection, strength of character
Goat's Rue – Reason
Golden Rod – Precaution
Gorse (Furze or Whin) – Anger
Grass – Utility; submission

Harebell – Happy retirement
Hawthorn – Hope
Hazel – Reconciliation
Heath – Solitude
Heliotrope – Devotion, faithfulness
Hellebore – Scandal; calumny
Henbane – Defect
Hepatica – Confidence
Hibiscus – Delicate beauty
Holly – Foresight
Hollyhock – Ambition; fecundity
Honesty – Honesty; fascination
Honeysuckle – Devoted affection
Hortensia – You are cold
Hyacinth – Sport, game, play
Hydrangea – A boaster; heartlessness

Ice Plant – Rejected; your looks freeze me
Iris – I have a message for you
Ivy – Friendship; fidelity; matrimony

Jasmine, Cape – Transport of joy

Jasmine, Indian – I attach myself to you

Jasmine, Spanish – Sensuality

Jasmine, White – Amiability

Jasmine, Yellow – Grace and elegance

Jonquil – I desire a return of affection

Juniper – Succour; protection

Kingcup – I wish I was rich

Laburnum – Forsaken; pensive beauty

Lady's Slipper Orchid – Fickleness; capricious beauty

Larkspur – Lightness, levity

Larkspur, Purple – Haughtiness

Larkspur, Pink – Fickleness

Laurel – Glory

Laurel, Mountain – Ambition

Laurestinus – A token. I die if neglected

Lavender – Distrust

Lilac, Purple – The first emotions of love

Lilac, White – Purity; modesty; youth

Lily, Day – Coquetry

Lily, Imperial – Majesty

Lily, White – Purity and sweetness

Lily, Yellow – Falsehood

Lily of the Valley – Return of happiness

Lobelia – Malevolence

London Pride – Frivolity

Love-in-a-Mist – Perplexity

Love-Lies-Bleeding – Hopeless, not heartless

Lucerne – Life

Lupin – Voraciousness; imagination

Magnolia – Love of nature

Mallow – Mildness

Mallow, Marsh – Mild disposition, beneficence

Mallow, Syrian – Consumed by love

Mallow, Venetian – Delicate beauty

Mandrake – Horror

Maple – Reserve

Marigold – Grief or pain

Marjoram – Blushes

Meadowsweet – Neglected beauty

Mesembryanthemum – Laziness

Mignonette – Your qualities surpass your charms

Mimosa – Courtesy

Mint – Virtue

Mistletoe – I surmount all difficulties

Mock Orange – Counterfeit

Moonwort – Forgetfulness

Moschatel – Weakness

Moss – Maternal love

Mouse-eared Chickweed – Ingenuous simplicity

Mullein – Good nature

Mustard Seed – Indifference

Myrrh – Gladness

Myrtle – Love

Narcissus – Egotism, self-esteem

Nasturtium – Patriotism

Nettle, Stinging – Cruelty

Olive Branch – Peace

Orange Blossom – Chastity. Your purity equals your lovliness

Orchid – A beauty, a belle

Palm – Victory

Pansy – Thoughts

Pasque Flower – You are without pretension

Passion Flower – Belief

Peach Blossom – I am your captive

Pennyroyal – Flee away
Peony – Shame; bashfulness
Peppermint – Warmth, cordiality
Periwinkle, Blue – Pleasures of
  memory
Periwinkle, Red – Early friendship
Periwinkle, White – Pleasant
  recollections
Phlox – Unanimity
Pimpernel, Scarlet – Assignation;
  change
Pine – Pity
Pine, Pitch – Philosophy
Pine, Spruce – Hope in adversity
Pink – Boldness
Pink, Carnation – Woman's love
Pink, Indian Double – Always lovely
Pink, Indian Single – Aversion
Pink, Mountain – Aspiring
Pink, Red Double – Pure and ardent
  love
Pink, Variegated – Refusal
Pink, White – You are fair and
  fascinating
Polyanthus – Pride of riches
Polyanthus, Crimson – The heart's
  mystery
Polyanthus, Lilac – Confidence
Poppy – Consolation
Primrose – Early youth, or forsaken
Primula – Diffidence
Privet – Defence

Quaking Grass – Agitation
Queen's Rocket – Fashionable. You
  are the queen of coquettes.

Ragged Robin – Wit
Ranunculus – I am dazzled by your
  charms

Reeds – Music
Rest Harrow – Obstacle
Rhododendron – Danger
Rose – Beauty
Rose, Austrian – Thou art all that is
  lovely
Rose, Bridal – Happy love
Rose, Burgundy – Unconscious
  beauty
Rose, Cabbage – Ambassador of love
Rose, Campion – Only deserve my
  love
Rose, Carolina – Love is dangerous
Rose, China – Grace
Rose, Christmas – Tranquillize my
  anxiety
Rose, Daily – Thy smile I aspire to
Rose, Damask – Freshness
Rose, Deep Red – Bashful shame
Rose, Dog – Pleasure and pain
Rose, Guelder – Winter; age
Rose, Hundred-Leaved – Pride
Rose, Japan – Pity
Rose, York and Lancaster – War
Rose, Maiden Blush – If you love me,
  you will find it out
Rose, Mundi – Variety
Rose, Musk – Capricious beauty
Rose, Musk, Cluster – Charming
Rose, White – Silence
Rose, Yellow – Decrease of love
Rose, White and Red Together –
  Unity
Roses, Crown of – Reward of virtue
Rosebud, Moss – Confession of love
Rosebud, Red – You are young and
  beautiful
Rosebud, White – Girlhood, and a
  heart ignorant of love
Rosemary – Affectionate
  remembrance

Rudbeckia (Black-Eyed Susan) – Justice
Rue – Disdain

Saffron – Do not abuse; beware of excess
Saffron Crocus – Mirth
Sage – Esteem
Scabious – Unfortunate love
Sensitive Plant – Timidity, delicate feelings
Shamrock – Light heartedness
Snapdragon – Presumption
Snowball – Thoughts of heaven; purity
Snowdrop – Hope
Sorrel – Affection
Sorrel, Wild – Wit ill-timed
Sorrel, Wood – Joy
Southernwood – Jest, bantering
Sowbread – Diffidence
Spearmint – Warmth of sentiment
Speedwell, Germander – Facility
Spider Wort – Esteem, but not love
Star of Bethlehem – Guidance; purity
Stock – Lasting beauty
Stock, Ten-Week – Promptness
Stonecrop – Tranquility
Strawberry Tree (or Arbutus) – Esteem and love
Strawberry, Wild – Perfection
Sunflower, Dwarf – Adoration
Sunflower, Tall – Haughtiness
Sweet Pea – Pleasure
Sweet William – Gallantry
Syringa – Memory
Syringa, Carolina – Disappointment

Tansy – I declare against you

Teasel – Misanthropy
Tendrils of Climbing Plants – Ties of Love
Thistle, Common – Austerity
Thistle, Scotch – Retaliation
Thrift – Sympathy
Tiger Flower – For once may pride befriend me
Traveller's Joy – Safety
Tulip, Red – Declaration of Love
Tulip, Variegated – Beautiful eyes
Tulip, Yellow – Hopeless Love

Valerian, Red – Accommodating disposition
Venus's Looking-Glass – Flattery
Vernal Grass – Poor, but happy
Veronica – Fidelity in friendship
Vetch – Shyness
Vervain – Enchantment
Vine – Intoxication
Violet, Sweet – Modesty
Virginia Creeper – Ever changing

Wallflower – Fidelity in misfortune
Weigela – Accept a faithful heart
White Water Lily – Purity of heart
Wisteria – I cling to thee
Woodbine – Fraternal love
Woodruff – Modest worth

Xeranthemum – Cheerfulness under adversity

Yew – Sorrow

Zephyr Flower – Expectation
Zinnia – Thoughts of absent friends

State Flowers of the USA

American Beauty Rose – District of Columbia
Apple Blossom – Arkansas, Michigan
Arbutus – Massachusetts
Bitterroot – Montana
Black-Eyed Susan – Maryland
Bluebonnet – Texas
Blue Iris – Tennessee
California Poppy – California
Carnation – Ohio
Cherokee Rose – Georgia
Coast Rhododendron – Washington
Columbine – Colorado
Flowering Dogwood – Virginia, North Carolina
Forget-Me-Not – Alaska
Goldenrod – Alabama, Kentucky, Nebraska
Great Laurel – West Virginia
Hawthorn – Missouri
Hibiscus – Hawaii
Indian Paintbrush – Wyoming
Lilac – New Hampshire

Magnolia – Louisiana, Mississippi
Mistletoe – Oklahoma
Mock Orange – Idaho
Mountain Laurel – Connecticut, Pennsylvania
Orange Blossom – Florida
Oregon Grape – Oregon
Pasque Flower – South Dakota
Peach Blossom – Delaware
Peony – Indiana
Pine Cone and Tassel – Maine
Red Clover – Vermont
Sagebrush – Nevada
Saguaro – Arizona
Sego Lily – Utah
Showy Lady's Slipper – Minnesota
Sunflower – Kansas
Violet – Illinois, New Jersey, Rhode Island, Wisconsin
Wild Rose – Iowa, New York, North Dakota
Yellow Jessamine – South Carolina
Yucca – New Mexico

Index

Page numbers in **bold** refer to colour plates, and in *italic* to black and white illustrations.